ELECTRONIC MODULES AND SYSTEMS
FOR BEGINNERS

C000202483

Other Titles of Interest

ELECTRONIC MODULES AND SYSTEMS
FOR BEGINNERS

by

OWEN BISHOP

**BERNARD BABANI (publishing) LTD
THE GRAMPIANS
SHEPHERDS BUSH ROAD
LONDON W6 7NF
ENGLAND**

Please Note

Although every care has been taken with the production of this book to ensure that any projects, designs, modifications and/or programs etc. contained herewith, operate in a correct and safe manner and also that any components specified are normally available in Great Britain, the Publishers do not accept responsibility in any way for the failure, including fault in design, of any project, design, modification or program to work correctly or to cause damage to any other equipment that it may be connected to or used in conjunction with, or in respect of any other damage or injury that may be so caused, nor do the Publishers accept responsibility in any way for the failure to obtain specified components.

Notice is also given that if equipment that is still under warranty is modified in any way or used or connected with home-built equipment then that warranty may be void.

© 1989 BERNARD BABANI (publishing) LTD

First Published – December 1989
Reprinted – October 1992
Reprinted – April 1995

British Library Cataloguing in Publication Data
Bishop, O. N. (Owen Neville) 1927 –
    Electronic modules and systems for beginners
    1. Electronic modules. National Centre for
      School Technology
    I. Title
    621.3815'3

ISBN 0 85934 211 5

Printed and bounded in Great Britain by Cox & Wyman Ltd, Reading

Contents

Chapter 1

MODULES AND SYSTEMS

Most circuit diagrams in electronics magazines and handbooks
are too complicated for a beginner to understand. The first
step toward understanding the diagrams is to be able to
recognise the symbols used for the electronic components. If
there are symbols in Figure 1 that you do not recognise, there
is a chart in Appendix A (p.190) to help you. Having dis-
covered what components are used in this circuit, can you say
what the circuit *does*? This is where the modular approach to
electronic circuits will help.

What is a module?

The circuit of Figure 1 is part of a home security system.
When it is operating, we arrange for a beam of light to fall on
the light-dependent resistor (or LDR). As long as the beam of
light is reaching the LDR, nothing happens. But, if the beam
of light is broken, the relay contacts are closed and the buzzer
sounds. When set up as a security system, the circuit detects
when an intruder passes between the source of light and the
LDR, and then sounds the alarm.

It is easier to understand how this circuit works if we think
of it as being made up of three parts, or *modules* (Fig.2). Each
module is a self-contained section of the circuit, with its own
particular function. Let us look at these modules in turn and
see what they do.

The *light sensor module* detects the beam of light. Since
the beam of light is something outside the circuit that acts on
the light sensor, we say that the beam of light is the *input* to
this module. So that the light sensor module can operate on
the next module, the transistor switch, the light sensor module
has an *output*. The output of the light sensor module is the
voltage at point A (Fig.2). This voltage is relatively high (2V
or more) when light is falling on the LDR. Exactly *why* it
is high is explained later (p.44), when we deal with this
module in detail. For the present, it is enough to know that
it *is* high. When the beam of light is broken by an intruder, no

Fig. 1 Home security system.

light falls on the LDR, and the output voltage becomes relatively low (less than 0.5V).

The second module in the circuit is the *transistor switch module*. This too has an input and an output. The output voltage from the light sensor module (at A) is the *input* voltage of the transistor switch module. When its input is low, the transistor is off, and the output of this module (at B, Fig. 2) is high. Conversely, when its input is high, its output is low.

Finally we come to the third module, the *relay driver module*. The input of this module is the voltage level at B produced by the transistor switch module. When this is low, the transistor of the relay driver is off, and no current flows through the transistor or the relay coil. The switch contacts of the relay are open. When the input is high, the transistor is

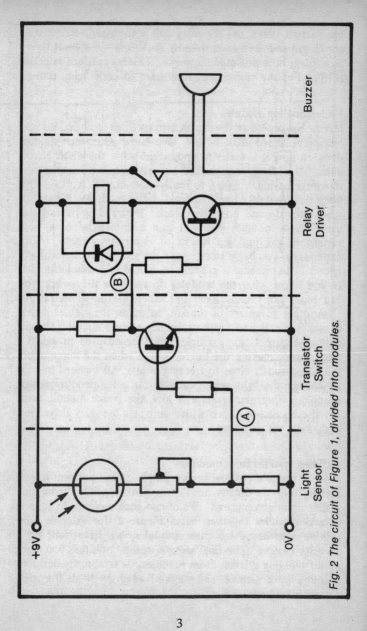

Fig. 2 The circuit of Figure 1, divided into modules.

Buzzer

Relay Driver

B

Transistor Switch

A

Light Sensor

+9V

0V

3

on, current flows, and the relay coil is energised. Its contacts are closed and the buzzer sounds. As before, we are not trying to explain how this module *works*. This is explained later, on p.139. For the moment we only need to know what it *does*.

Understanding modules

Having broken down the circuit into its three modules, it looks less complicated than before. We know what each module does, so now it is easier to understand what the whole circuit does. Also, since each module has relatively few components, it would be much easier to understand how it works. This book describes 60 commonly used circuit modules. It explains what they do and how they work. By building, testing and using these modules you will gain a knowledge of a wide variety of the building blocks of electronic circuits. With experience, you begin to recognise the separate sections of any circuit — to visualise it as being composed of distinct modules. If you know what the modules do and how they work, you can more easily understand the action of the whole circuit.

Another advantage of thinking in terms of modules is that it makes it easier to adapt or modify a given circuit. The circuit of Figure 1, for example, could be adapted to act as a frost alarm, making the buzzer sound when the temperature falls dangerously close to freezing point. All we need to do is to change the light sensor module for a temperature sensor module. When temperature is low, the sensor module turns off the transistor switch which activates the relay driver and makes the buzzer sound.

Building systems from modules

Since a module is usually very simple, it can perform only a simple job. We usually need a circuit that will do something rather more complicated. We obtain such a circuit by joining several modules together, as in Figure 2, for example. By joining together these three modules, we have built up a security *system*. The final section in the book tells you more about building systems from modules. Several ready-designed systems are described, and ways of adapting them for other purposes are suggested.

4

Whether we are adapting an existing circuit or designing a completely new one, it always helps to use the modular approach. It is not necessary to worry too much about the *details* of the modules at the design stage. We are concerned only with what the modules *do*. In designing the security system of Figure 1, for example, we could begin with quite a simple diagram (Fig.3). This is known as a *system diagram*.

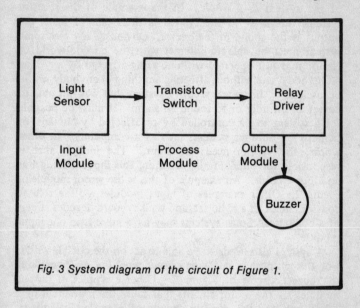

Fig. 3 System diagram of the circuit of Figure 1.

It shows what modules are used and how they relate to each other. At the design stage it is not necessary to know exactly what form the various modules will take. We can think about such details later. For example, the light sensor module might be based on an LDR, or on a photodiode or on a photo-transistor. Light sensor modules of all three kinds are des-cribed in this book. Having decided that the system requires a light sensor of some kind, we later select one of these types. Which type we select depends on features such as its sensi-tivity, reliability, cost, power requirements, and the avail-ability of its components.

5

Inputs and outputs

In the discussion of Figure 2 it was shown that each module in a system has an *input* and an *output*. This is a minimum condition. Some modules described in this book have more than one input and some have more than one output.

There is another way in which these terms 'input' and 'output' are used. This is when we refer to inputs or outputs of the system *as a whole*. In the example of the security system, the input to the system is the beam of light; the output is the sound of the buzzer. Obviously any electronic system must be able to interact with the outside world. A circuit that just operated without being affected by anything or anybody, and without affecting anything or anybody would be useless. Imagine a security system that was not able to detect an intruder or to sound an alarm! It must be possible for a system to be controlled by or affected by humans (or perhaps by another system, such as a computer). In other words, the system needs an input. The module that is responsible for obtaining or detecting this input is known as an *input module*. An example of this is the sensor module of Figure 2. Other examples of input modules are the volume control circuit of a radio set, and the keyboard decoder circuit of a computer. Some systems may have more than one input module.

A system also needs to be able to act on the outside world. For this purpose it needs an *output module*. An example is the buzzer circuit of Figure 2. Other examples of output modules are the motor circuits that cause the movement of a robot arm, or the display circuits of a pocket calculator.

It is possible to have a system that consists simply of an input module and an output module, but most systems are more complicated than this. For example, the sensor module of Figure 2 is not able to operate a relay directly. Its requires a transistor switch to do this for it. We call the transistor switch a *process module*. The process it performs is to amplify the power level, so that a small change in voltage of the output of the sensor produces a larger voltage change that can make the relay operate. We can therefore think of the security system circuit as consisting of three parts: INPUT – PROCESS – OUTPUT.

Figure 3 shows the security system analysed in this way. Most systems can be analysed in this way, though in many there may be several process modules, and possibly several input and output modules too.

To help you find the modules to use for system building, the modules in this book are listed under three main headings:

> Input modules
> Process modules
> Output modules

There is one other main heading, the *power supply modules*. The process modules have been sub-divided into two groups, according to whether the processing is done by analogue circuits or by digital circuits. The difference between the two processing techniques is explained later.

Chapter 2

BUILDING MODULES

There are three main ways in which modules can be built:

1 Breadboard
A breadboard is a way of temporarily building up components into a circuit. The wire leads of components are plugged into small sockets. Figure 4 shows the arrangement of the sockets of a typical small breadboard. In the drawing the sockets are represented by small squares. The lines joining the squares show that the sockets in the central area of the board are connected to each other in groups of five. The sockets along each edge of the board are also connected. Connections may also be made by wire links. Figure 5 shows how to assemble the light sensor module on a breadboard.

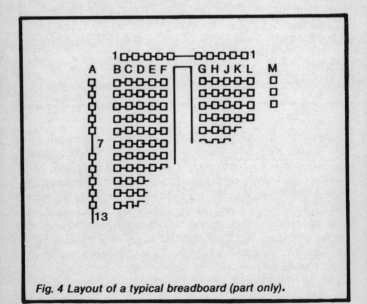

Fig. 4 Layout of a typical breadboard (part only).

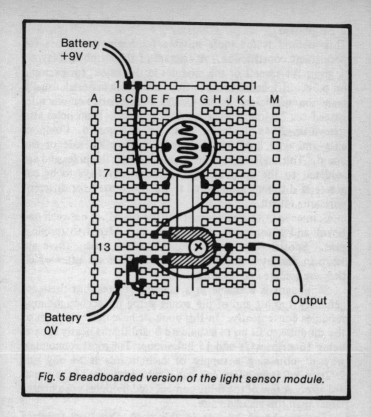

Battery
+9V

A B C D E F G H J K L M

1 ───────────────────── 1

7

13

Output

Battery
0V

Fig. 5 Breadboarded version of the light sensor module.

Breadboarding is very useful for trying out the circuit of a
module before building it in more permanent form. It is useful sometimes to breadboard a module that you may need
only on one or two occasions. It is also useful when designing
new modules and deciding on the exact values of components
required. Breadboarding has the advantage that components
can be removed and re-used in other modules. However,
breadboards are intended only for temporary circuits. If a
module is to be used repeatedly, one of the other methods of
construction is preferable.

9

2 Stripboard

This method is the most suitable for beginners to use for permanent construction. A diagram of the stripboard layout is given for several of the modules in this book, for example on p.38. Stripboard is made from insulating material, usually resin-bonded plastic. It has parallel copper strips on one side, spaced on 2.54mm (0.1in) centres and with 1mm holes also spaced on 2.54mm centres, as shown in Figure 6. Components and wire links are mounted on the plain side of the board. The leads or wire links pass through the holes and are soldered to the copper strips. A strip may have to be cut across if different sections of it are to be used for different parts of a circuit.

Connections to components off the board, or between one board and another are made by wires soldered to terminal pins. Special stripboard terminal pins are used. These are 1mm in diameter, and fit tightly into the holes, after which they are soldered to the strips.

Stripboard is available in a number of sizes, but these are generally too big and of the wrong shape for accommodating modules conveniently. In this book we have designed most of the modules to fit on to a standard board that is nearly square, being 16 strips wide and 15 holes long. The most economical way of obtaining a supply of such boards is to buy one 292mm x 95mm board and cut it into 14 pieces of the standard size. A few of the more complicated modules need boards larger than this standard size.

The stripboard layouts in this book also have standard positions for the power supply rails and for the input and output terminals (Fig.6). This makes it easier to connect several boards together when building up a system. Usually inter-board connections will be temporary, so supply lines and input terminals are provided with leads terminated by crocodile clips. A series of boards can readily be joined together as in Figure 7. The supply rails run continuously along the top and bottom edges of the board. On most boards, the positive supply (+9V) runs along the top strip (strip A) while the ground rail (0V) runs along the strip O. Some modules require a negative supply (−9V) in addition, for which strip P is used.

10

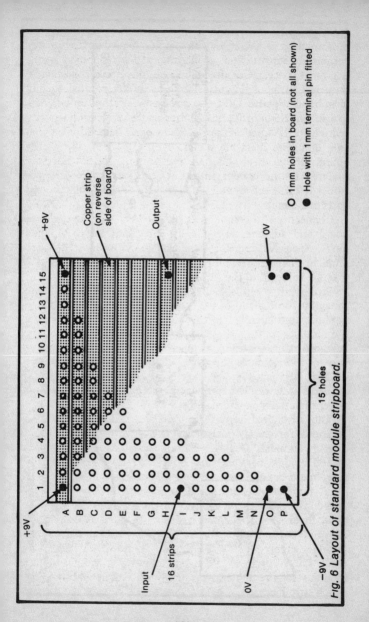

Fig. 6 Layout of standard module stripboard.

11

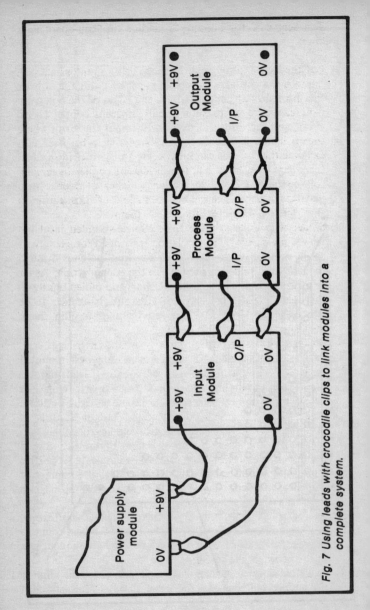

Fig. 7 Using leads with crocodile clips to link modules into a complete system.

12

The sequence for building a module on strip-board is as follows:

1. Cut the board to the required shape using a junior hacksaw. Smooth the cut edge with glass paper or a fine file. Check that no flakes of copper strip at the edges of the board are bent across so as to short-circuit adjacent copper strips.

2. Use a spot face cutter or twist-drill to cut the strips where shown in the layout diagram. When a strip has been cut, examine the cut ends carefully, using a magnifier if possible. It is very easy for a hair-thin bridge of copper to remain, still connecting the two sections. Flakes of copper strip may also lie across the gap between adjacent strips causing a short circuit. Look for and remove these.

3. Solder wire links in place first. Single-stranded insulated wire is preferable. The insulation is stripped for a length of about 5mm at each end before inserting the ends through the holes and soldering the ends to the copper strips. As far as possible these wires should be short and pulled tightly to the board before soldering. If adjacent strips have to be connected, a blob of solder can be used to join them, instead of a wire link.

4. Solder resistors in position, after bending their leads carefully at right angles. Usually resistors are best mounted flat and as close as possible to the board. If leads have to be soldered to holes only 1 or 2 strips apart, it may be necessary to mount the resistors in the upright position.

5. Solder terminal pins and integrated circuit sockets in position. Normally the strips beneath an i.c. socket are cut, so as to isolate pins on opposite sides of the i.c. But, if the circuit requires opposite pins to be connected, the strip joining these pins is *not* cut. This reduces the number of wire links needed. Check carefully on the layout diagram to see if any strips should remain uncut.

6. Mount and solder other components, such as transistors, diodes and capacitors. It is advisable to clip a heat-shunt to the leads of transistors and diodes (on the component side of the board) while soldering them.

7. Solder inter-board connecting wires and crocodile clips to the supply rail pins and the input pin(s). Multi-stranded

insulated wire is preferred. Crocodile clips have plastic insulating sleeves in different colours. Standardise the colours, using red for the +9V supply, blue for the ground supply (0V), black for the −9V supply and yellow or green for input/output connections. An easy way of preparing these leads is to buy a ready-made test lead kit. This consists of 10 or more leads terminated at both ends with a crocodile clip. Cut the leads in half, and strip the cut ends. Solder the cut ends to the terminal pins on the boards.

Methods for building complete systems on a single stripboard are outlined in Chapter 6.

3 Printed circuit board

In this technique we begin with an insulated board, made of resin-bonded plastic or glass-fibre, coated with copper on one side. Double-sided boards, with copper on both sides, can also be used, but the technique is rather more difficult and the circuits of these modules are not complicated enough to make double-sided boards worth attempting.

The first step in making a pcb is to prepare the design. You need to have all the components available so that you know their dimensions and the spacing between their leads. The design is best worked out first on squared paper. Mark the positions of the terminal pins, where the components are to be placed and where their leads are to come. At this stage the design may look like Figure 8.

The next step is to prepare the design that is eventually to be transferred to the copper, ready for etching. Since this design will be on the *under-side* of the board, it is inverted with respect to the component layout design, as shown in Figure 9. Write a '+' on the design beside each point that is to be directly connected to the positive supply. Write a 'G' beside each point that is to be connected to the ground rail. If there is to be a negative (−9V) supply, mark these points too. Draw lines joining any other points that are to be joined together.

It is best if the final design consists of large areas of copper at +9V, large areas at 0V and (if appropriate) large areas at

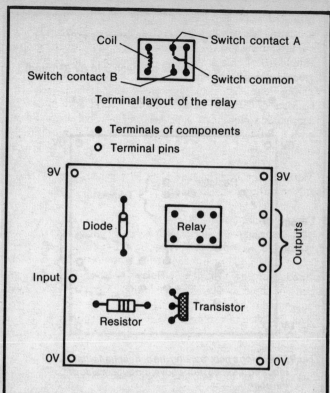

Coil

Switch contact A

Switch contact B

Switch common

Terminal layout of the relay

● Terminals of components
○ Terminal pins

9V

Diode

Relay

Outputs

Input

Resistor

Transistor

0V

9V

0V

Fig. 8 Designing a pcb: planning the layout of components
(as seen from above, the component side of the board).

−9V. These large areas are preferred because the etching
solution will last longer and because they allow more copper
for the conduction of the bigger currents that flow in the
supply lines. It may be possible to alter the layout, moving
the components around to allow these areas to be made as
large as possible. At the same time, look for instances where
lines joining one pair of points cross lines joining another pair
of points. Crossings have to be made by using a wire link
instead of a copper track, but it is better to avoid this situation

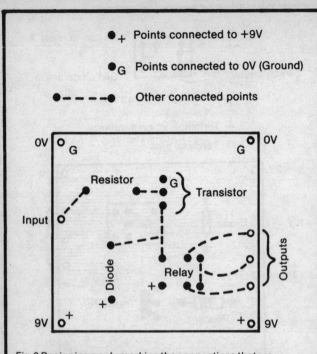

● + Points connected to +9V

● G Points connected to 0V (Ground)

●– – – –● Other connected points

Fig. 9 Designing a pcb: marking the connections that are
required (as seen from above, the copper side of
the board).

by re-arranging the components, if possible. A few wire links
may be unavoidable in a complicated module. At this stage,
check the design very carefully, making sure that all the connections have been made, and have been made correctly.
Where connections go to terminals of transistors or integrated
circuits, remember that they must show these as seen from the
underside of the board. Careful checking is essential because
mistakes are difficult to correct once the board has been made.

The final version of the design (Fig.10) has large areas for
the power lines. The areas have rounded corners. The tracks
and pads are neatly arranged and drawn, and the number of

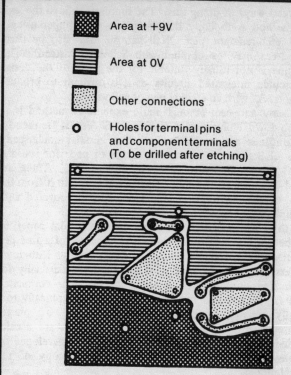

Area at +9V

Area at 0V

Other connections

O Holes for terminal pins
   and component terminals
   (To be drilled after etching)

Fig. 10 Designing a pcb: the finished design ready for etching
(as seen from below, the copper side of the board).

wire links is reduced to a minimum (there are none in this
example). The positions where holes are to be drilled in the
board for component wires and terminals are clearly marked.
Check the dimensions again carefully and finally check once
again that all the connections are correct.

Before you transfer the design to copper, the surface of
the copper must be scrupulously cleansed. Use a brand of
household cleaner or a special pcb cleaner. From now on, the
board must be handled only by its edges to prevent¯grease
from fingers interfering with the etching. When the board is

17

dry, transfer the design to the surface of the copper. There are several ways of doing this. The simplest, though the least tidy, method is to copy the design on the copper using a special etch-resistant pen. Nail varnish may also be used. Large areas may be covered with Sellotape instead. This technique is not usually suitable for the parts of the design that include integrated circuits, as it is difficult to produce narrow tracks with an etching pen or nail varnish.

An easy and neat (though more expensive) method is to use rub-down etch-resistant transfers. Sheets of frequently-used outlines are available, including circular solder-pads, groups of 3 pads for transistors, arrays of pads for ics, and straight tracks and corners of various widths. These are rubbed down on to the copper surface and protect it from the action of etching fluid. Large areas may be covered with Sellotape or painted with nail varnish, as above.

A third technique is to draw the design on paper, as described above, but using black ink. The use of a fine pen and ruler makes it easy to draw the tracks neatly. Rub-down transfers may also be used with this method, especially for complicated outlines such as those for ics. The completed design is checked and then transferred photographically to a specially-prepared copper-clad board with a photo-sensitised coating. Instructions for doing this are usually included in the kit of materials. When this is developed by suitable chemicals it leaves an etch-resistant copy of the original design.

Rub-down transfers usually have a small clear dot at the centre of each solder-pad. When the board is etched, the copper is etched at this point. The small depression so formed helps to guide the drill bit to the exact point for drilling the hole. Use a fine centre-punch to mark the positions of all other holes that will have to be drilled later. This perforates the etch-resistant material so that a small dot is etched away at each hole.

With any of these three methods, the next step is to etch way the copper where it is not covered by etch-resistant material. This leaves the circuit design, consisting of tracks and pads of copper. It is best to buy an etching kit and follow the instructions provided with it.

When the board has been etched and the resistant material removed, using a solvent or abrasive, the holes are drilled. A 1mm drill is suitable for terminal pins and most wire leads. Certain components, such as preset resistors, may require holes of a larger diameter. From then on, assembly follows steps 3 to 7 as described for stripboards.

Chapter 3

MODULES

This chapter describes over 60 modules commonly used in electronics. All modules operate on 9V dc, which can be provided by a battery (Module 1). This avoids the problems associated with constructing mains-powered circuits. However, you may prefer to use a ready-made mains power supply unit instead of a battery, as these are cheaper to operate in the long run. Mains PSUs are inexpensive and are often sold under the name of 'battery eliminators' for powering small radios and tape-recorders. Often they consist of a large plug-head which fits into a standard 13-amp mains socket, with the PSU enclosed in the plug-head. The maximum current supplied by such units is usually 300mA or 400mA. This is more than enough for most of the modules described here. Take care not to overload the mains PSU, since this may burn out its transformer. The specification for each module tells you how much current it requires.

The modules are listed under these headings, to help you find the kind of module you require:

     A Power supply modules
     B Input modules
     C Process modules — (i) Analogue
                        (ii) Digital
     D Output modules

To start with you will need a power supply module. Read through the descriptions in section A and decide which module or modules you need. When you have built the power supply, you are ready to go ahead with building other modules or systems.

If you decide to begin at the module level, choose any one of the modules in sections B, C or D. Building it and testing it will teach you a lot about it. Then choose and build other modules. Gradually you will acquire a collection of modules from which you can assemble a wide variety of systems, as described in Chapter 5.

You may be impatient and want to start straight away with a fully-fledged electronic system. If so, skip ahead to Chapter 5 and look at the system diagrams shown there. When you have found one you would like to build, come back to this chapter and construct the 3 (possibly more) modules that you need for it.

Module descriptions

For each module, the following information is given, as appropriate:

Function: what it does, and how to use it.

Circuit diagram: this helps you recognise the same or similar arrangement of components when seen in circuit diagrams in magazines or in other electronics books.

How it works: this explains the electronics theory behind the simple circuit units, and helps you to see how to design similar circuits to suit your own requirements.

Parts required: your shopping list. **All resistors are carbon or equivalent, 0.25W, 5% tolerance** unless otherwise specified, although superior types, such as 0.6W metal film, 1% tolerance, can be substituted if preferred. A standard stripboard is used unless otherwise stated.

Stripboard layout: how to set it out on one of the standard stripboards (p.10), and any special constructional points. There may be a *diagram* to show you how to lay out the components or there may be a *table* to tell you where to mount the components on the standard module board (Fig.6) and what wired connections to make. There is also a list of the points (if any) at which the copper strips must be cut across, and a list of points that are to be joined by blobs of solder beneath the board. **All modules require leads terminated in crocodile clips on the +9V, 0V, and −9V rails, and on the input terminal(s).**

As explained in Chapter 2, you can also assemble the module on a breadboard or design and etch your own pcb.

Power requirements: supply voltage required and how much current it uses.

Input specification: exactly what input it requires.

Output specification: exactly what output it supplies.

Modifications: suggestions for simple variations on the circuit.

21

A – POWER SUPPLY MODULES

1 Battery Box

Function: to provide a 9V direct current supply for powering the modules and systems described in this book.

Circuit diagram: see Figure 11.

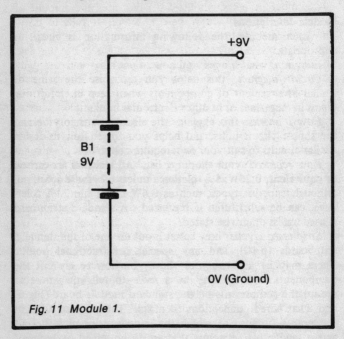

Fig. 11 Module 1.

Parts required: battery box to house six size 'D' dry cells, crocodile clips (2 off, red + blue).

Stripboard layout: no stripboard required. Solder a flexible lead about 20cm long to each terminal. Preferably use red wire for the positive terminal and blue wire for the ground (0V). Solder a crocodile clip (red/blue) to the free ends of the leads.

Output specification: the voltage is nominally 1.5V per cell, but falls with use. The total current supplied depends upon the type of cell used (incidentally *never* mix cell types, or mix

22

old cells and new cells of the same type):

Cell type	Current supplied
zinc-carbon	5.2Ah at 39 ohms for 4h/day
zinc chloride	7.5Ah at 39 ohms for 4h/day
alkaline	12.4Ah at 10 ohms for 2h/day

The number of ampere-hours (Ah) indicates the amount of current the cell can supply before its voltage falls to 0.9V. This is based on the rate of use (determined by the circuit to which it is connected) and the number of hours use per day. The table above indicates the load (in ohms) and the daily usage when the different types of cell were being tested.

From these figures you can estimate the amount of power obtained from a cell of a given type. For example, a circuit requiring 50mA (0.05A) uses 0.05Ah if it runs for 1 hour. Thus a supply of 5.2Ah (from a zinc-carbon cell) lasts for 5.2/0.05 = 104 hours. Note that this calculation is independent of the number of cells in the battery box. If the circuit supplies high current *continuously*, rather than for 4h/day, the cell becomes exhausted more rapidly than this.

The cost of the different types of cell must be taken into account. The cheapest cells are the zinc carbon type. Zinc chloride cells are more expensive to buy than zinc carbon cells, but they last longer. Alkaline cells are the most expensive but last even longer and can be used to supply larger currents. In the long run, the alkaline cells are the most satisfactory of the types listed above.

As an alternative, you could consider using a battery made from lithium cells. These are available as a small PP3-sized battery, which is connected to the circuit by a battery clip. Lithium batteries are more expensive than the other types, but last far longer. They are ideal for portable equipment and for devices that require small currents for periods of months or years. You may find these useful for powering permanent systems that you build.

2 Negative Voltage Generator
Function: provides a negative voltage supply for devices such as operational amplifiers. You can use this with Module 1 to obtain a split +9V supply (see also Module 4).

23

Circuit diagram: see Figure 12.

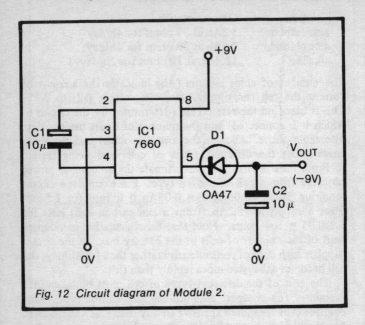

Fig. 12 *Circuit diagram of Module 2.*

How it works: the circuit is based on the 7660 voltage converter ic. This contains an oscillator operating at about 10kHz. It also contains four MOS power transistors, acting as switches, and a logic network to turn the switches on or off at the correct times. The diagrams in Figure 13 show the circuit with the transistor switches drawn as ordinary switches.

There are two stages to the operation. In stage A, capacitor C1 is charged to the supply voltage, V, since S1 and S3 are closed. The potential of plate a is V. The potential of plate b is 0V. Their potential difference (p.d.) is V. In stage B, S1 and S3 are open, but S2 and S4 are closed. The potential of plate a immediately falls by V volts to 0V. But the p.d. across a capacitor tends to remain unchanged. This means that the potential of plate b also falls by V volts, taking it from 0 to −V. Plate c of C2 is also forced to the same potential. Thus, if no current is drawn from the output terminal, V_{OUT}

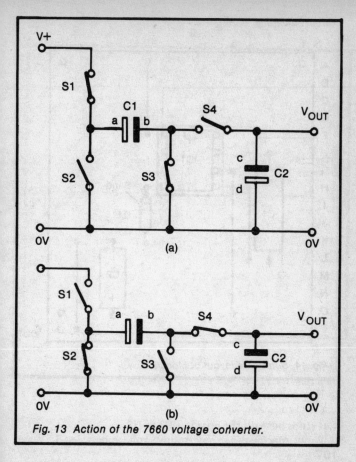

Fig. 13 *Action of the 7660 voltage converter.*

is −V. The process is repeated so that, as current is drawn from V_{OUT}, the negative charge on C2 is maintained. The amount of current that can be drawn from V_{OUT} is limited by the rate at which charge is transferred to C2.

Parts required: C1, C2 electrolytic capacitors 10μ, 16V or 25V, D1 germanium diode OA47, IC1 7660 voltage converter, 8-pin d.i.l. socket, 1mm terminal pins (5 off), crocodile clips (2 off, red + blue).

Stripboard layout: see Figure 14.

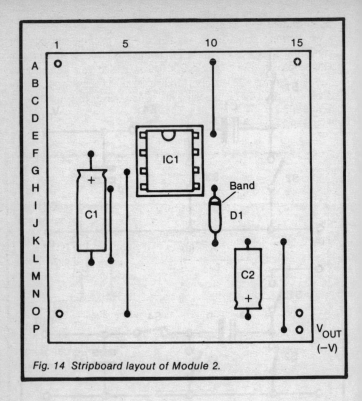

Fig. 14 Stripboard layout of Module 2.

Cut strips beneath the board at E7 to H7.

Input specification: any positive voltage between 3.5V and 10V.

Output specification: output voltage equals *minus* the input voltage, provided only a small current is drawn. Output voltage drops with increasing current, as if there was a 70 ohm resistor in series with the output. For example, if the output current is 20mA and supply voltage is 9V, the drop in output voltage is 70 x 0.02 = 1.4V. Thus the output voltage is only −7.6V.

3 Regulated +5V Supply

Function: generates a regulated +5V supply, suitable for powering logic ics of the TTL family. The logic modules in this book use the CMOS 4000 series which can be powered directly from a 9V supply (Module 1). On occasions you may wish to use TTL instead, in which case this module is required.

Circuit diagram: see Figure 15.

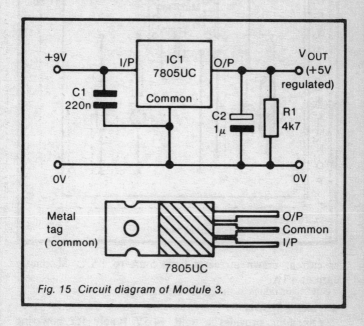

Fig. 15 Circuit diagram of Module 3.

Parts required: R1 4k7, C1 220n polyester, C2 1μ tantalum, IC1 7805UC 5V voltage regulator, heat sink to be bolted to metal tag of IC1, 1mm terminal pins (5 off), crocodile clips (2 off, red + blue).

Stripboard layout: see Figure 16.

Input specification: any positive voltage in the range 7.2V to 35V.

Output specification: output voltage +5V ±0.2V. Increases by 3mV over input voltage range 7V to 25V. Falls by 15mV

27

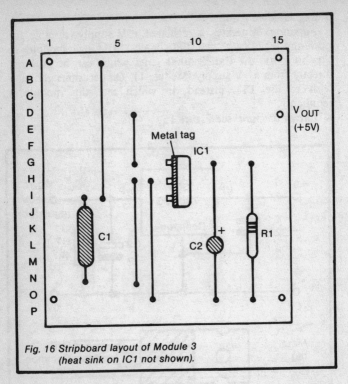

Fig. 16 Stripboard layout of Module 3
(heat sink on IC1 not shown).

as current drawn increases from 5mA to 1.5A. Maximum
current = 1A.

4 Voltage Splitter

Function: provides a split +4.5V supply for powering
operational amplifiers. It is intended for use with a 9V mains
PSU. If your supply is a battery (Module 1), it is simpler and
more economic of power to obtain the split supply by connecting a lead between the 3rd and 4th cell in the battery box,
as shown in Figure 17b.

Circuit diagram: see Figure 17.

How it works: this circuit is a potential divider (see explanation for Module 9) with two equal resistors. The potential
of the middle rail is exactly mid-way between that of the two

28

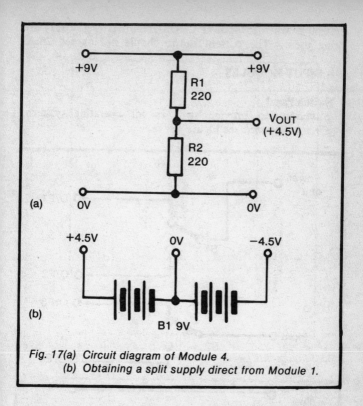

Fig. 17(a) Circuit diagram of Module 4.
(b) Obtaining a split supply direct from Module 1.

supply rails. If the supply is 9V, from Module 1, the middle rail is at 4.5V. When using operational amplifiers we refer to the middle rail as 0V, in which event the positive supply rail is +4.5V relative to the middle rail and the ground supply rail is −4.5V.

Parts required: R1, R2 220 ohm 0.6W metal film resistors, 1% tolerance, 1mm terminal pins (5 off), crocodile clips (2 off, red + blue).

Power requirements: the resistor chain passes 21mA when operated.

Input specification: any voltage up to 9V.

Output specification: the voltage of the mid-rail is half of the supply voltage, assuming that only small currents are

29

drawn, as when low-power CMOS amplifiers (e.g. 7611) are being used. The current drawn should not exceed 2mA.

B – INPUT MODULES

5 Switch Panel
Function: to provide switches for operating systems.
Circuit diagrams: see Figure 18.

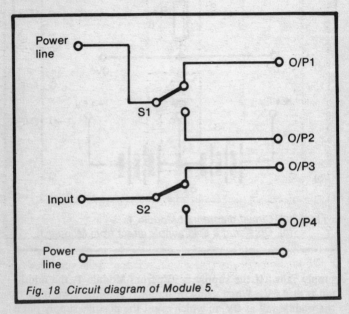

Fig. 18 Circuit diagram of Module 5.

How it works: the suggested layout provides two single-pole double throw switches. Panels with other types of switches can be built up in a similar way. The suggested layout has one switch connected to a power rail, the +9V rail if orientated as shown in Figure 19. The board can be turned round so that this switch is connected to the 0V rail instead.

Parts required: S1, S2 miniature SPDT slide switches (e.g. Electromail stock no. 339-673), 1mm terminal pins (9 off), crocodile clips (3 off, red + green + blue).

Stripboard layout: see Figure 19.

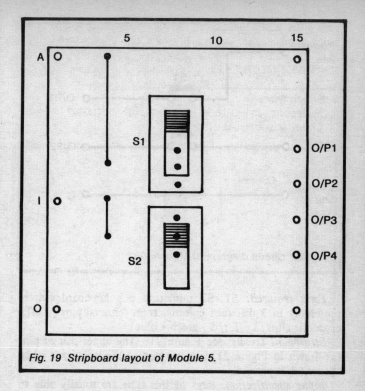

Fig. 19 Stripboard layout of Module 5.

Input specification: switches of the type suggested are rated to switch up to 30V dc at up to 4A.

6 Key Panel

Function: to provide keys with momentary action for operating systems.

Circuit diagram: see Figure 20.

How it works: the suggested layout provides two push-to-make key-switches. Panels with other types of switches can be built up in a similar way. The suggested layout has one key connected to a power rail, the +9V rail, if orientated as shown in Figure 21. The board can be turned round so that this key is connected to the 0V rail instead.

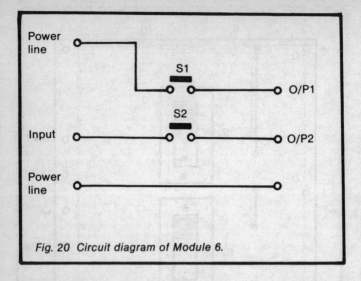

Fig. 20 Circuit diagram of Module 6.

Parts required: S1, S2 miniature pcb keyboard switch, preferably in 2 different colours, 1mm terminal pins (7 off), crocodile clips (3 off, red + green + blue).

Stripboard layout: see Figure 21. The upper pair of pins (as drawn in Figure 21) is connected to the lower pair when the switch is pressed.

Input specification: keys of this type are usually able to switch up to 100V ac at up to 100mA, with a limit of 6VA (i.e. the voltage multiplied by the current should not exceed 6 volt-amps).

7 Debounced Key

Function: this is intended for controlling logic-based systems. An ordinary key-switch gives a series of connections and disconnections (contact-bounce) when it is pressed or released. Although contact-bounce is not necessarily a problem, it may cause faulty operation of certain circuits. This module produces a single clean transition from one state to the other. The output state is indicated by an LED.

Circuit diagram: see Figure 22.

How it works: when the key (S1) is not being pressed, the

32

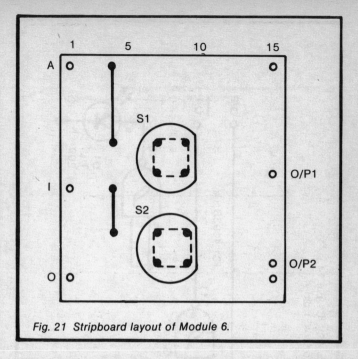

Fig. 21 Stripboard layout of Module 6.

inputs to gate 1 are both held high by R1. Its output is low; this appears at the O/P terminal. Capacitor C1 has a p.d. of 9V across it. When S1 is pressed, the voltage across C1, and also at the inputs to gate 1, falls steadily almost to zero. When it reaches about 3.5V, the gate input now counts as a logic low input. The output of the gate changes instantly to logic high. Once this change has occurred, any small rise in input voltage does *not* make it change back again. This is because the gate has Schmitt inputs. For the gate to change back to its original state, the input voltage would have to rise to about 5.3V. This is not likely to happen, even if the switch momentarily closes again. Thus the gate output changes once only when the key is pressed. When the key is released, the voltage across C1 rises. As it reaches 5.3V the gate changes state. After that it cannot change back again, unless the voltage falls back to 3.5 or less, which is not likely to happen. Again, there is a

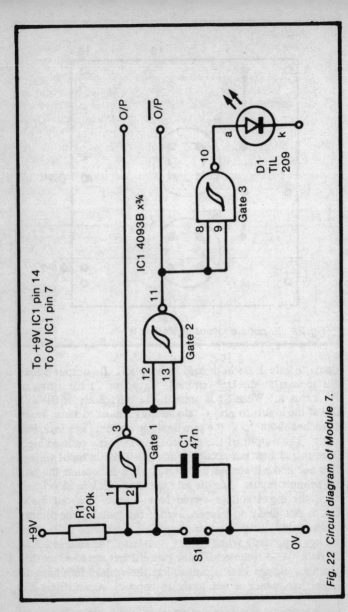

Fig. 22 Circuit diagram of Module 7.

34

clean transition.

The output of gate 1 is inverted by gate 2, to give output $\overline{O/P}$, which is normally high but goes low when S1 is pressed. The output of gate 2 is inverted by gate 3, the output of which drives an LED. The LED comes on when S1 is pressed.

Parts required: R1 220k, C1 47n polyester capacitor, D1 TIL209 or similar LED, IC1 4093B CMOS quadruple NAND gate with Schmitt trigger inputs, S1 miniature pcb keyboard switch, 14-way d.i.l. socket, 1mm terminal pins (6 off), crocodile clips (2 off, red + blue).

Stripboard layout: see Figure 23. Cut strips beneath the board at C7, D7, F7 to I7 (but NOT E7). Solder blobs join

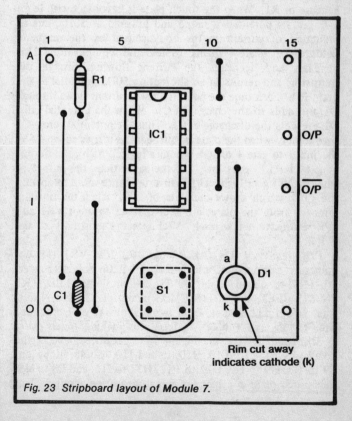

Fig. 23 Stripboard layout of Module 7.

C6 to D6, G6 to H6 to I6, D9 to E9, H9 to I9.

Power requirements: 9V. 20mA when LED is on; no current when it is off.

Output specification: Logic levels compatible with CMOS.

8 Touch Switch

Function: for controlling logic-based systems by touch. This module, like module 7, produces a bounce-free output.

Circuit diagram: see Figure 24.

How it works: TR1 is a junction field-effect transistor (JFET). When a current is passing through it, a voltage is generated across R2, and thus the source terminal (s) is at a small positive potential. The gate (g) is held at zero potential because of R1. When the touch plate is in contact with (e.g.) a finger, its potential is raised and lowered at 50Hz, due to induction of current in the body caused by the magnetic fields from nearby mains cables and equipment. This increases and decreases the current flowing through the transistor, and results in an alternating 50Hz potential at the drain (d). Each time the potential rises, current flows through D1 and adds to the charge on C1. When the potential falls, D1 prevents the discharge of C1. Thus the potential across C1 rises rapidly when the plate is touched. As it rises above 4.5V, the input to gate 1 of IC1 becomes logical 'high', the output of gate 1 ($\overline{O/P}$) goes low. At the same time, the output of gate 2 (O/P) goes high. O/P is inverted twice more to operate the LED, which shows the state of O/P. When the finger is removed from the plate, C1 is discharged through VR1 and O/P returns to a low level. VR1 sets the sensitivity of the switch.

Parts required: R1 10M, R2 6k8, R3 10k, VR1 1M subminiature carbon horizontal preset, C1 220n polyester layer, D1 1N4148 silicon diode, D2 TIL209 or similar LED, TR1 2N3819 JFET, IC1 4011B CMOS quadruple 2-input NAND gate, 14-pin d.i.l. socket, 1mm terminal pins (6 off), crocodile clips (2 off, red + blue), material for making touch plate.

Stripboard layout: see Figure 25. Cut strips beneath the board at C10, D10, F10, H10, I6 and I10. Solder blobs join C9 to D9, G9 to H9, D12 to E12, H12 to I12, and L8 to M8. The touch plate is a piece of metal measuring about 2–3cm

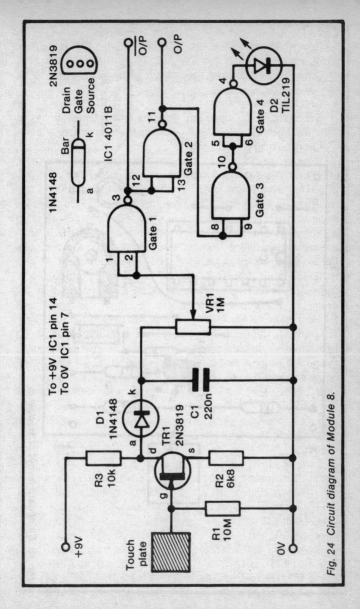

Fig. 24 Circuit diagram of Module 8.

37

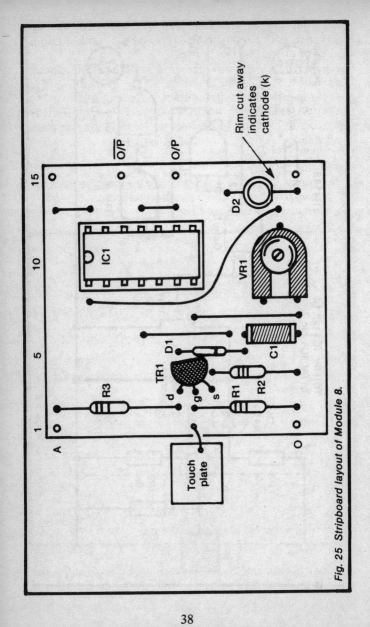

Fig. 25 Stripboard layout of Module 8.

38

square, but can be any shape and size, as determined by experiment. A large thumb-tack (drawing-pin) pushed into a wooden or plastic base can be used.

Power requirements: 9V dc. 1mA when quiescent, 18mA when plate is touched (mainly to operate the LED).

Input specification: finger touches the touch-plate.

Output specification: normally output is low and LED is off. Rises to high and LED comes on for as long as the plate is touched.

9 Potential Divider

Function: to produce a variable output voltage between 0V and the supply voltage. To act as a position sensor.

Circuit diagram: see Figure 26.

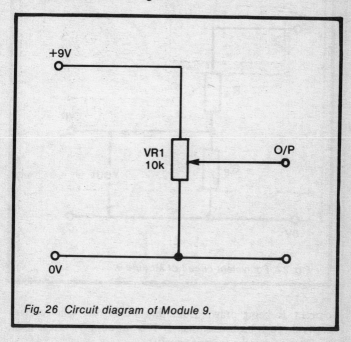

Fig. 26 Circuit diagram of Module 9.

How it works: one end of the resistance track is at 0V, the other is at the supply voltage (usually 9V). As the wiper is

39

moved from the 0V end of the track to the supply voltage end, the voltage at the wiper (or O/P) rises steadily from 0V to the supply voltage. The potentiometer knob may be adjusted to produce any required voltage in the range 0V to 9V. Alternatively, the spindle of the potentiometer may be attached to an external mechanism. O/P varies according to the amount by which the mechanism turns the spindle. By using a module to measure O/P, we can measure the amount by which the spindle has been turned. In this way the potential divider acts as a position sensor.

We can consider the potentiometer at any given setting to consist of two resistors in series (Fig.27). Assuming that no

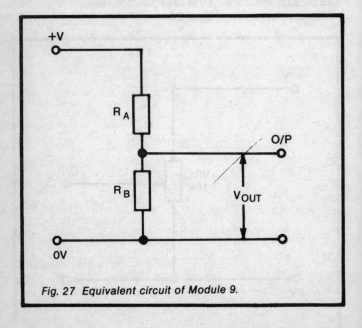

Fig. 27 Equivalent circuit of Module 9.

current is being drawn from the circuit, the same current flows through both resistors. If V is the supply voltage then, by Ohm's Law, the current equals:

40

$$I = \frac{V}{R_A + R_B}$$

If V_{OUT} is the output voltage then, by Ohm's Law:

$$I = \frac{V_{OUT}}{R_B}$$

Combining these two equations, we get:

$$\frac{V}{R_A + R_B} = \frac{V_{OUT}}{R_B}$$

Rearranging terms gives:

$$V_{OUT} = \frac{V \times R_B}{R_A + R_B}$$

This equation applies to all circuits or parts of circuits in which two resistors are connected in series. The circuit is known as a *potential divider*.

In the case of this module, V is constant and so is the sum of R_A and R_B (10k). Thus V_{OUT} is proportional to R_B, the resistance of the part of the track between the wiper and the 0V end.

Parts required: VR1 10k rotary carbon potentiometer, crocodile clips (3 off, red + blue + white), knob for VR1.

Stripboard layout: no stripboard required. If the connections are as shown in Figure 28, O/P of the central terminal increases as the knob is turned clockwise.

Power requirements: passes 0.9mA when on a 9V supply.

Input specification: with most potentiometers of this type the spindle rotates 270° between one end of the track and the other.

Output specification: voltage variable between 0V and the supply voltage. O/P for any given position of the wiper is

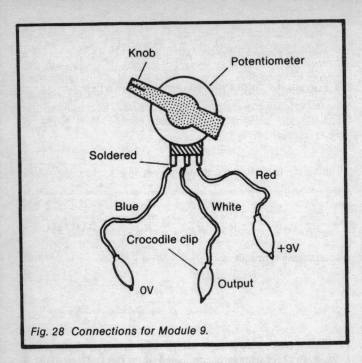

Fig. 28 Connections for Module 9.

reduced as a larger current is drawn. Current in excess of
90μA (one-tenth of the current passing through the resistor)
causes an appreciable fall in O/P.

Modifications: the module is improved by mounting the
potentiometer on the lid of a small plastic case. Leads are
taken out through a hole in the side of the case. Two or
more potentiometers may be mounted in the same case, if
several modules of this kind are in use.

Potentiometers of other values may be used instead.
Potentiometers of lower value (1k or 100 ohms) allow a larger
current to be drawn, but also require a larger current. A 100
ohm potentiometer should be of the high-power cermet or
wire-wound type, rated at 1W or more. Potentiometers of
higher resistance (100k or 1M), take very little current but
supply very little current. They are suitable for providing a
variable input voltage to high-impedance devices, such as to

42

the inputs of CMOS operational amplifiers.

10 Light Level Sensor (LDR type, version 1)

Function: to produce a varying output depending on the amount of visible light falling on the light-dependent resistor. This module is slower acting than Modules 12 and 13, though it is fast enough for most purposes. It is less affected by short-lived changes in light intensity and therefore less likely to trigger 'false alarms'.

Circuit diagram: see Figure 29.

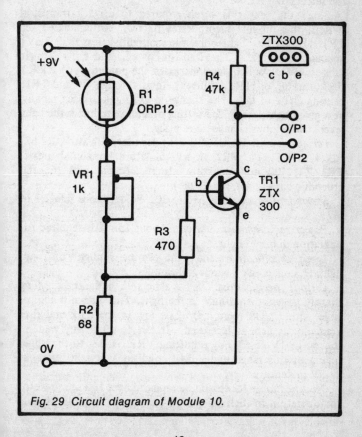

Fig. 29 Circuit diagram of Module 10.

43

How it works: R1 is a light-dependent resistor (LDR), the resistance of which decreases as the amount of light falling on it is increased. In the dark, the resistance of the LDR is about 1M. It falls to about 250 ohms in normal room lighting and to only 20 ohms in bright sunlight. R1, VR1 and R2 form a potential divider (see Fig.27) in which R1 corresponds to R_A and VR1 plus R2 correspond to R_B. Since the resistance of R1 is reduced as light increases, the potential at the junction of R1 and VR1 rises. This potential is available directly as O/P2. O/P2 can be adjusted at a given light level by varying the setting of VR1.

Since the sensor is often required to drive a transistor switch, this module incorporates its own switch, based on TR1. Under low light only a low potential (less than 0.6V) appears across R2. The transistor is off, and O/P1 is high (almost 9V). As light level increases, the potential at VR1/R2 rises, turning on TR1. Current flows through R4 and TR1, causing O/P1 to fall. The change in O/P1 takes place rapidly at a given light level. The setting of VR1 determines the light level at which this change takes place.

Parts required: R1 ORP12 light-dependent resistor, R2 68, R3 470, R4 47k, VR1 1k sub-miniature horizontal preset, TR1 ZTX300 npn transistor, 1mm terminal pins (6 off), crocodile clips (2 off, red + blue).

Stripboard layout: see Figure 30. Solder blobs join L7 to M7.

Power requirements: 9V dc. About 15mA is required for operation in bright light.

Input specification: the light can be sunlight or room lighting, including oil lamps and candles.

Output specification: O/P1 is almost 9V in darkness, falling sharply to less than 20mV in the light. This output is compatible with CMOS logic. O/P2 is low in the dark and rises gradually as light is increased. It can be set to any value in the range 1V to 7V, by adjusting VR1. If set to the upper region of this range under light conditions, it falls by about 2−3V in darkness.

Modifications: R2 should be replaced by a 100 ohm resistor for operation in high light levels (sunlight). See also Module 11.

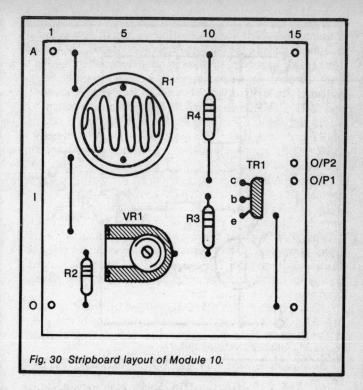

Fig. 30 Stripboard layout of Module 10.

11 Light Level Sensor (LDR type, version 2)

Function: as for Module 10, but operating in the opposite sense.

Circuit diagram: see Figure 31.

How it works: this works in the same way as Module 10, but since the LDR corresponds to R_B of Figure 27, the outputs operate in the opposite sense.

Parts required: R1 ORP12 light-dependent resistor, R2 4k7, R3 47k, VR1 10k sub-miniature horizontal preset, TR1 ZTX300 npn transistor, 1mm terminal pins (6 off), crocodile clips (2 off, red + blue).

Stripboard layout: Wire links – J14 to O14, C2 to K2. R1 – K5 to O5. R2 – C8 to I8. R3 – A10 to H10. VR1 – A3, C3 and B7 (wiper). TR1 – H12 (c); I12 (b); J12 (e). Terminal pins

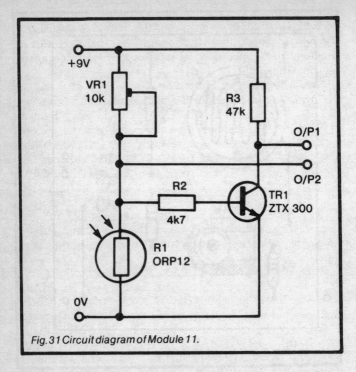

Fig. 31 Circuit diagram of Module 11.

— A1, A15, C15, H15, O1, O15. Solder blob joins B3 to C3.

Power requirements: 9V dc. 1mA in the dark, 70mA in sunlight.

Input specification: sunlight or room lighting.

Output specification: O/P1 is almost 9V in the light, falling sharply to less than 20mV in the dark. This output is compatible with CMOS logic. O/P2 is low in the light and rises gradually as light is decreased. It can be set to any value in the range 0.1V to 7V, by adjusting VR1. If set to the upper region of this range under dark conditions, it falls by about 2–3V as light increases.

12 Light Level Sensor (photodiode type)

Function: to detect infra-red radiation, giving a high or low logical output depending on the level of radiation received.

46

This sensor has a faster action than Modules 10 and 11. Since IR is invisible to the human eye, this sensor is particularly suited for use in intruder-detection systems. It is also suited to remote control applications, as it is less affected by change in ambient visible light.

Circuit diagram: see Figure 32.

How it works: the sensor is a photodiode which is reverse-biassed. Thus only a very small leakage current passes through it. This is of the order of a few nanoamps in darkness, increasing to a few microamps when receiving IR. This provides the base current for TR1. VR1 passes an additional small current, allowing the response level to be adjusted. TR1 is part of a Schmitt trigger circuit (see Module 30). With no IR, TR1 is off, TR2 is on and O/P is low. With sufficient IR, the increased base current to TR1 turns it on, turning TR2 off and causing O/P to rise to high. Since this is a Schmitt trigger circuit, its action is to produce a sharp change in output at the selected IR level.

Parts required: R1 330k, R2 330, R3, R5 1k (2 off), R4 4k7, R6 68, VR1 1M sub-miniature horizontal pre-set, D1 TIL100 infra-red photodiode, TR1, TR2 ZTX300 npn transistor (2 off), 1mm terminal pins (5 off), crocodile clips (2 off, red + blue).

Stripboard layout: Wire links — A8 to F8, C1 to E1, E2 to L2. R1 — L4 to O4. R2 — I7 to L7. R3 — A9 to G9. R4 — G11 to I12. R5 — A12 to H12. R6 — J12 to O12. VR1 — A3, C3 and B7 (wiper). D1 — E3(a), F3(k). TR1 — G10(c), I10(b), J10(e). TR2 — H13(c), I13(b), J13(e). Terminal pins — A1, A15, H15, O1, O15. Cut strip beneath the board at I11. Solder blob joins B3 to C3.

Power requirements: 9V dc. 15mA in dark; 9mA when irradiated.

Input specification: with D1 mounted as described it is sensitive to radiation coming from the left. Peak response at 940nm. Sources of IR include sunlight, filament lamps, IR LEDs (see Module 64).

Output specification: 9V in dark, less than 1V when irradiated. Output is CMOS compatible.

Modifications: sensitivity and directional response may be increased by enclosing D1 in a tube or small case, with a converging lens to focus incident radiation on its sensitive surface.

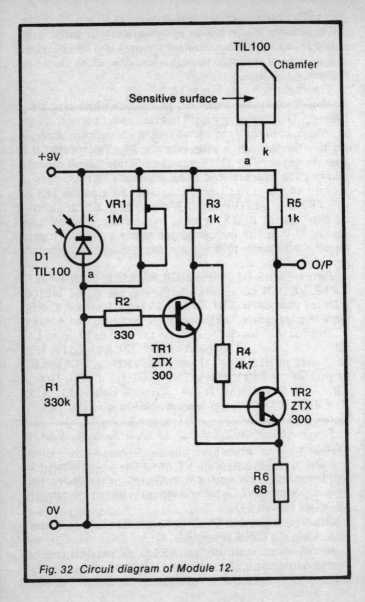

Fig. 32 Circuit diagram of Module 12.

48

13 Light Level Sensor (phototransistor type)

Function: to detect changes in visible light levels and produce a varying output voltage. This sensor is very fast-acting and operates well at low light intensity.

Circuit diagram: see Figure 33.

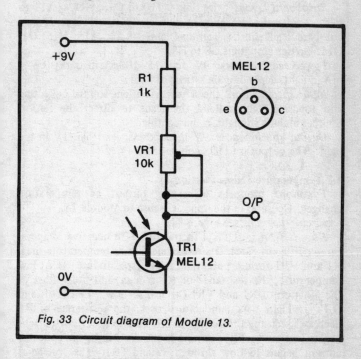

Fig. 33 Circuit diagram of Module 13.

How it works: when light falls on the base of the photo-transistor, charge carriers are released. The action of light is thus equivalent to a supply of base current, and its effect is the same – to cause an increase in collector current. The MEL12 comprises two transistors connected as a Darlington pair (see Module 31), so a low level of light produces a large collector current and the device is highly sensitive. When the collector current flows through R1 and VR1 a potential difference appears across them, causing a fall in output voltage, proportional to light intensity. Output voltage is adjusted by using

VR1. Although the MEL12 has a base terminal, this is not used in this module.

Parts required: R1 1k, VR1 10k sub-miniature horizontal preset, TR1 MEL12 photo-Darlington, 1mm terminal pins (5 off), crocodile clips (2 off, red + blue).

Stripboard layout: wire link – J10 to O10. R1 – A12 to F12. VR1 – F8, H8 and G4 (wiper). TR1 – H12(c), J12(e), cut base lead short. Terminal pins – A1, A15, H15, O1, O15. Solder blob joins G8 to H8.

Power requirements: 9V dc. 15–100μA in dark; 0.7–4 mA in light, depending on setting of VR1.

Input specification: the sensor has a lens top for collecting and focusing light. Bend the leads to direct the sensor. Sources include sunlight, room lighting.

Output specification: 9V in darkness; less than 1V in the light. The output is CMOS compatible.

14 Temperature Sensor (version 1)

Function: produces a varying output as temperature changes. Operates in the opposite sense to Module 15.

Circuit diagram: see Figure 34.

How it works: R1 is a thermistor, with negative temperature coefficient (ntc). Its resistance falls as temperature rises. R1 and VR1 form a potential divider (see Module 9). At low temperature, the resistance of R1 is high, and the voltage at the junction of R1 and VR1 (= O/P2) is low. TR1 is off and O/P1 is high. As temperature rises, the resistance of R1 decreases, causing the voltage at R1/VR1 to rise. Base current begins to flow to TR1, turning it on. As it turns on, collector current begins to flow through R3 and TR1. The voltage at the junction R3/TR1 (= O/P1) falls. The temperature at which TR1 turns on is set by adjusting VR1.

Parts required: R1 bead type thermistor, 47k at 25°C, R2 470, R3 1k, VR1 100k sub-miniature horizontal preset, TR1 ZTX300 npn transistor, 1mm terminal pins (6 off), crocodile clips (2 off, red + blue).

Stripboard layout: wire links – A8 to D8, F8 to M8, J13 to O13. R1 – D6 to F6. R2 – I9 to M9. R3 – A13 to H13. VR1 – M3, O3 and N7 (wiper). TR1 – H11(c), I11(b), J11(e). Terminal pins – A1, A15, F15 (O/P1), H15 (O/P2), O1, O15.

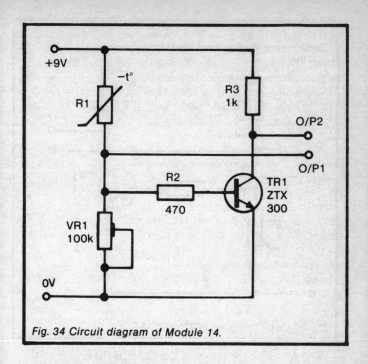

Fig. 34 Circuit diagram of Module 14.

Solder blob joins N7 to O7.

Power requirements: 9V dc. 0.2mA when temperature low (0°C), 10mA when temperature high (100°C).

Input specification: temperature range is approximately −40°C to 110°C. Response time is 1.5s.

Output specification: O/P1 increases gradually as temperature rises; is 0−1V at 25°C, depending on the setting of VR1. O/P2 is 9V at low temperature, swinging sharply to 1V (approx.) at high temperature. O/P2 is CMOS compatible.

Modifications: R1 may be mounted on the board, or at the end of a flexible lead.

15 Temperature Sensor (version 2)

Function: produces a varying output as temperature changes. Operates in the opposite sense to Module 14.

Circuit diagram: see Figure 35.

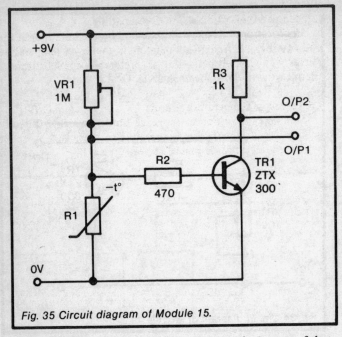

Fig. 35 Circuit diagram of Module 15.

How it works: the action of the circuit is the inverse of that of Module 14.

Parts required: R1 bead type thermistor, 47k at 25°C, R2 470, R3 1k, VR1 1M sub-miniature horizontal preset, TR1 ZTX300 npn transistor, 1mm terminal pins (6 off), crocodile clips (2 off, red + blue).

Stripboard layout: wire links — A8 to D8, F8 to M8, J13 to O13. R1 — M5 to O5. R2 — I10 to M10. R3 — A13 to H13. VR1 — D7, F7 and E3 (wiper). TR1 — H11(c), I11(b), J11(e). Terminal pins — A1, A15, F15 (O/P1), H15 (O/P2), O1, O15. Solder blob joins E7 to F7.

Power requirements: 9V dc. Up to 20mA, depending on the setting, but is generally less.

Input specification: temperature range is approximately −40°C to 110°C. Response time is 1.5s.

Output specification: O/P1 decreases gradually as temperature rises; can be set to be 9V at low temperature. O/P2 is

9V at high temperature, swinging sharply to 1V (approx.) at low temperature. O/P2 is CMOS compatible.

Modifications: R1 may be mounted on the board, or at the end of a flexible lead. For operation in the lower temperature ranges (25°C and below) it is preferable to substitute a thermistor with resistance 15k at 25°C.

16 Precision Temperature Sensor

Function: to produce a voltage output which is directly proportional to the Celsius temperature.

Circuit diagram: see Figure 36.

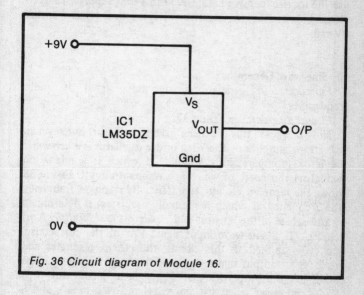

Fig. 36 Circuit diagram of Module 16.

How it works: the module is based on the LM35DZ ic which gives output voltage directly proportional to the temperature in degrees Celsius. If the temperature is $t°C$, the output voltage is $10t$ millivolts.

Parts required: IC1 LM35DZ precision temperature sensor, 1mm terminal pins (5 off), crocodile clips (2 off, red + blue).

Stripboard layout: wire links — A6 to G6, I6 to O6. IC1 — G8(V_S), H8(V_{OUT}), and I8(Gnd). Terminal pins — A1, A15,

H15, O1, O15.

Power requirements: 9V dc (the ic operates on any voltage from 4V to 30V). 56µA.

Input specification: temperature range 2°C to 100°C.

Output specification: V_{OUT} = 10t millivolts. Precision at 25°C is +0.6°C.

Modifications: for temperatures below 2°C, use a split supply; *either* +4.5V with a 91k resistor between V_{OUT} and the −4.5V rail, *or* +9V with a 180k resistor between V_{OUT} and the −9V rail. Output voltage is relative to the 0V rail. For increased range (−40°C to 110°C) and precision (+0.4°C) use the more expensive LM35CZ, with a split supply. Temperatures below 0°C give negative voltage output relative to the 0V rail.

17 Sine-wave Generator

Function: to generate a sine-wave signal at audio frequencies.

Circuit diagram: see Figure 37.

How it works: this is a Wien bridge oscillator, based on an operational amplifier. The Wien bridge oscillator is a *harmonic oscillator* (compare with Module 25 which is a relaxation oscillator) the heart of which is a resonant circuit. Figure 38 shows the resonant circuit separately. Its resonant frequency (the frequency at which it naturally oscillates) is determined by the values of the resistors and capacitors (see *Modifications* below). If a sine-wave input signal V_{IN} of the correct frequency is applied to this circuit, the circuit resonates and produces an output signal V_{OUT} of the same frequency. The circuit has the properties that V_{OUT} is in phase with V_{IN} (V_{OUT} increases when V_{IN} increases and *vice versa*), and is exactly one-third of V_{IN}. The amplifier is adjusted (by setting VR1) so that its gain is slightly greater than 3 (i.e. the value set on VR1 is just over 81k, three times the value of R3). Since V_{OUT} is fed to the non-inverting input of the amplifier (see Module 33), this provides positive feedback, keeping the circuit in oscillation (Fig.39). The output of the amplifier is *just over* 3 times V_{OUT} to allow for the small part of the signal being fed via C3 to the next module.

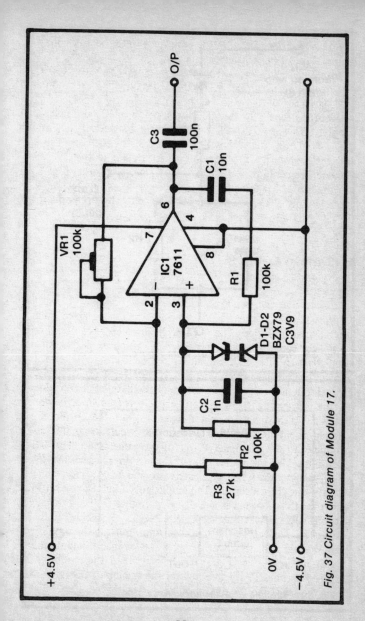

Fig. 37 Circuit diagram of Module 17.

55

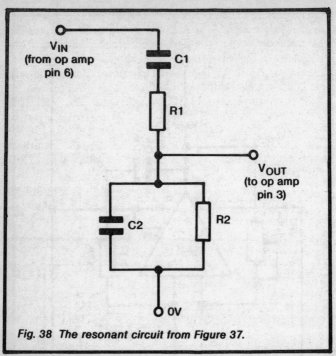

Fig. 38 The resonant circuit from Figure 37.

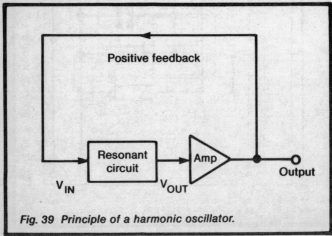

Fig. 39 Principle of a harmonic oscillator.

The gain of the amplifier must remain close to 3 if it is to oscillate continuously. If gain falls below 3, there is insufficient feedback to keep the resonant circuit oscillating. If it rises above 3, the waveform becomes clipped and is no longer a sine wave. Stability is maintained by the two Zener diodes D1 and D2, connected cathode to cathode.

Parts required: R1, R2 100k (2 off), R3 27k, VR1 100k sub-miniature horizontal preset, C1 10n polyester layer, C2 1n polyester layer, C3 100n polyester, D1, D2 BZX79C3V9 Zener diodes 3.9V (2 off), IC1 7611 CMOS operational amplifier, 1mm terminal pins (7 off), crocodile clips (3 off, red + blue + black).

Stripboard layout: see Figure 40. Cut strips beneath the board at G7 to J7, and H12. Solder blobs join C4 to D4, N8 to O8.

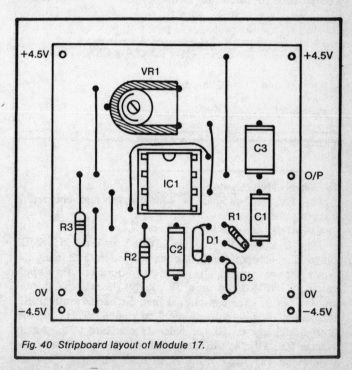

Fig. 40 Stripboard layout of Module 17.

To set up the circuit, connect a crystal earplug between the output terminal and the 0V rail. Turn VR1 to its minimum setting (anti-clockwise). No sound is heard. Very slowly turn VR1 clockwise until the tone suddenly begins and has a pure bell-like sound. This is the correct setting. Further turning of VR1 produces a louder sound but it is harsher owing to the clipping of the wave-form.

Power requirements: ±4.5V dc. 1mA in each power supply rail.

Output specification: frequency with the component values shown is approximately 500Hz. Maximum amplitude is ±3.9V.

Modifications: frequency can be altered by substituting other values for C1, between 2.2n (1kHz) and 100n (150Hz). The equation for calculating frequency is:

$$f = \frac{1}{6.28 \sqrt{R1 \times R2 \times C1 \times C2}}$$

If R1 = R2 and C1 = C2 this reduces to:

$$f = \frac{1}{6.28 \times R1 \times C1}$$

18 Astable Multivibrator

Function: to produce a square-wave, logic-compatible train of pulses.

Circuit diagram: see Figure 41.

How it works: the module is based on the 7555 CMOS timer IC. Current flows through R1 and R2, charging C1. When the p.d. across C1 reaches two-thirds of the supply voltage (i.e. 6V if run on a 9V supply) this is sensed by the chip at pin 6. The capacitor is then discharged through R2, the current flowing through pin 7 to ground. This continues until the charge on C1 has fallen to one-third of the supply voltage (i.e. 3V). As the charge falls just below this level, the trigger pin (2) triggers the ic to begin charging C1 again.

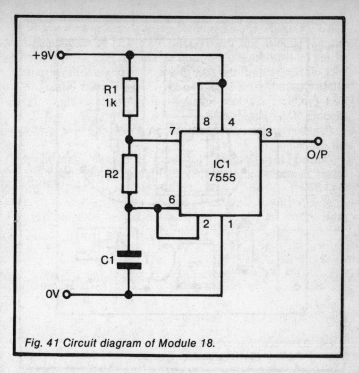

Fig. 41 Circuit diagram of Module 18.

Output at pin 3 is high while C1 is charging and low while it is discharging. The time taken to charge depends on the values of R1, R2 and C1:

$$t_c = 0.693 \, (R1 + R2) \, C1$$

The time taken to discharge depends on the values of R2 and C1:

$$t_d = 0.693 \, (R2) \, C1$$

The frequency of oscillation is given by:

$$f = 1.44/\{(R1 + 2R2) \, C1\}$$

Parts required: R1, R2 1k (2 off), VR1 100k miniature

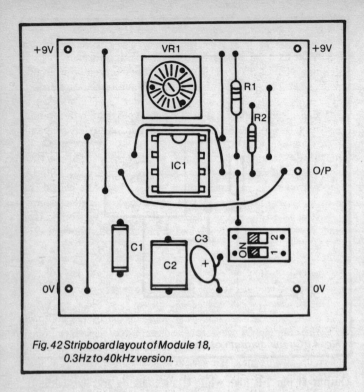

Fig. 42 Stripboard layout of Module 18, 0.3Hz to 40kHz version.

horizontal potentiometer with finger adjustment, C1 10n polyester layer, C2 470n polyester layer, C3 22μ tantalum, IC1 7555 CMOS timer, 8-pin d.i.l. socket, dual SPST d.i.l. switch, 1mm terminal pins (5 off), crocodile clips (2 off, red + blue).

Stripboard layout: see Figure 42 above. Cut strips beneath the board at F7 to I7, H13, L12, M12. Solder blobs join B13 to C13, K14 to L14 to M14, N4 to O4. Figure 42 shows a version of the module in which R2 and VR1 are in series, thus allowing the frequency to be varied. It also has 3 different capacitors which can be switched in to give three frequency ranges. C1 is permanently wired in for the highest range. C2 or C3 are switched in (in parallel with C1) to give the medium and low ranges. Frequencies obtainable are:

60

Range	Capacitors	Frequencies	Applications
Low	C1 + C3	0.3Hz to 21Hz	Lamp flashers
Medium	C1 + C2	15 Hz to 1021Hz	Timers, audio circuits
High	C1	716Hz to 40kHz	audio, ultrasonics

The capacitors must be low-leakage types and not ceramic.

Power requirements: 9V dc. 5mA approximately, depending on frequency.

Output specification: square-wave output, 0V to 9V, logic compatible. The ic output can sink up to 100mA.

Modifications: a single-range version can be made by omitting the d.i.l. switches and connecting a single capacitor between K13 and O13. A single-frequency version can be made by also omitting VR1 and connecting R2 between G12 and H12.

19 Crystal Clock

Function: to generate accurate timing pulses.

Circuit diagram: see Figure 43.

How it works: the 4060 ic contains most of the components for building an oscillator, and a complete 14-stage binary divider. If the crystal used has a frequency of 32.768kHz and is fed to the divider, the frequency obtained from the final (14th) stage is exactly 2Hz. If this is fed to a divide-by-two circuit (Module 46), a frequency of 1Hz is obtained.

Parts required: R1 10M, R2 100k, C1 10p polystyrene, VC1 50p miniature trimmer capacitor (or 65p), IC1 4060B CMOS 14-stage divider with oscillator, XTAL1 timing crystal, 32.768kHz, 16-pin d.i.l. socket, 1mm terminal pins (5 off), crocodile clips (2 off, red + blue).

Stripboard layout: wire links — A7 to D7, F2 to H13, I7 to M7, K2 to O2. R1 — I11 to J11. R2 — J9 to N9. C1 — M6 to O6. VC1 — M13, O13, and N10 (spindle). XTAL1 — M8 to N8. IC1 — D3 (pin 1) to K6 (pin 9). Terminal pins — A1, A15, H15, O1, O15. Cut strips beneath the board at D4 to K4, H10, M10.

Power requirements: 9V dc. 1mA.

Output specification: square wave (0V, 9V) at 2Hz. Accuracy is approximately 200 parts per million over the

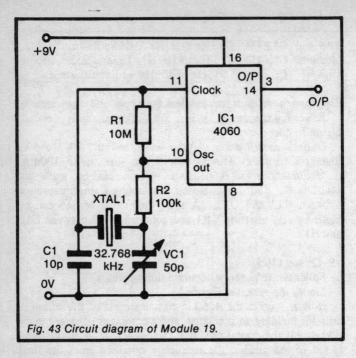

Fig. 43 Circuit diagram of Module 19.

temperature range $-10°C$ to $60°C$.

Modifications: crystals of other frequencies may be substituted, and the output can be taken from other stages of the counter. The pins for these stages are:

Stage	Divides by	Pin
4	16	7
5	32	5
6	64	4
7	128	6
8	256	14
9	512	13
10	1024	15
12	2048	1
13	8192	2
14	16384	3

20 Magnetically-operated Switch

Function: detects a magnetic field and operates a switch, which latches until a reverse field is detected.

Circuit diagram: see Figure 44.

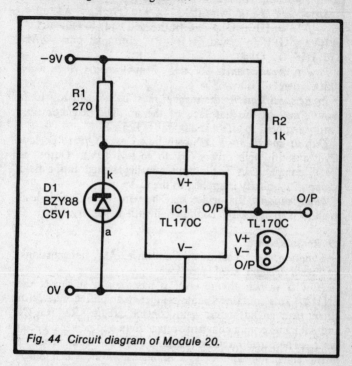

Fig. 44 Circuit diagram of Module 20.

How it works: the circuit is based on a device making use of the Hall effect. When a slice of suitable semi-conducting material is placed in a magnetic field, the electrons flowing in the material are deflected to one side. This causes a p.d. to develop between one side of the material and the other. This p.d. is detected by internal circuitry and made to operate a latching switch. The device operates on a 5V to 7V supply, so R1 and the Zener diode D1 are used to supply a constant operating voltage. The ic has an open-collector output, so it requires a pull-up resistor, R2.

Parts required: R1 270, R2 1k, D1 BZY88C5V1, Zener diode, 5.1V, IC1 TL170C Hall Effect switch, magnet to operate the ic (usually supplied with the ic), 1mm terminal pins (5 off), crocodile clips (2 off, red + blue).

Stripboard layout: wire links – G9 to O9. R1 – A4 to F4. R2 – A13 to H13. D1 – F6 (k, banded end) to O6. IC1 – F11(V+), G11(V−), and H11(O/P). Terminal pins – A1, A15, H15, O1, O15.

Power requirements: 9V dc. 25mA when O/P is high; 40mA when O/P is low.

Input specification: the magnet must be brought to within about 5mm of the flat face of the ic. The magnetic flux density required to affect the switch is ±25mT.

Output specification: a north pole causes O/P to go low (0V); a south pole causes O/P to go high (9V). Output is CMOS compatible. The output remains latched until a field of opposite polarity is applied to the ic.

Modifications: the device may be wired to a flexible lead to allow it to be used in conjunction with machinery.

21 Radio Receiver

Function: to receive medium-wave AM transmissions.

Circuit diagram: see Figure 45.

How it works: the receiver is based on a single ic, the ZN414. This contains a radio-frequency amplifier, a detector circuit and an automatic gain control circuit. R1–R3, C1 and TR1 make up a constant-voltage source to power the ic at pin 1. The tuned circuit consists of L1, a coil wound round a ferrite aerial rod, and VC1, a tuning capacitor, which allows the circuit to be tuned to oscillate at the radio frequency of the transmitting station.

Parts required: R1 220k, R2 82K, R3 1k5, R4 100k, C1, C3 100n polyester (2 off), C2 10n polyester, VC1 300p tuning capacitor, L1 see below, IC1 ZN414 AM radio ic, ferrite rod 10cm long, 1cm diameter, knob for VC1, 28swg or 30swg enamelled copper wire (about 3 metres length), stripboard 95mm x 63mm (24 strips by 37 holes, e.g. Vero 10346), 1mm terminal pins (5 off single-sided, 2 off double-sided), crocodile clips (2 off, red + blue), 4 nuts and bolts for mounting board.

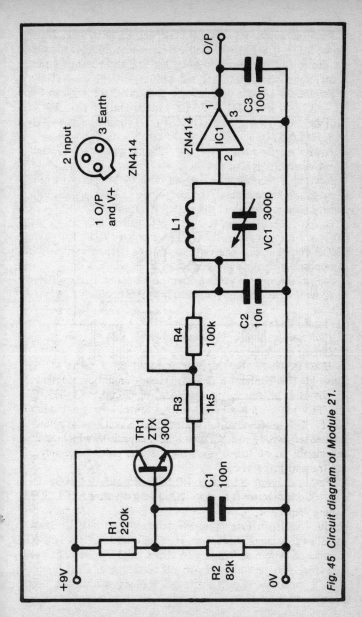

Fig. 45 Circuit diagram of Module 21.

65

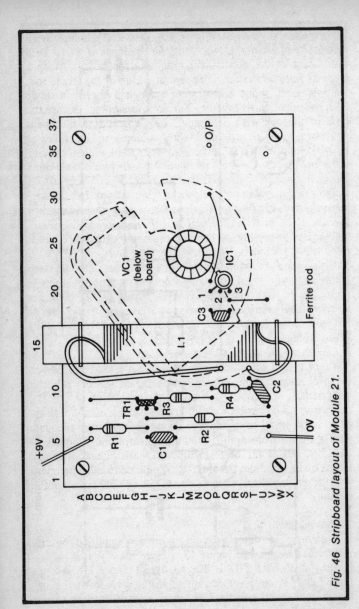

Fig. 46 Stripboard layout of Module 21.

66

Stripboard layout: see Figure 46. First drill a hole, 9.5mm diameter and centred at N24, to take the bush of VC1. Drill four holes at the corners for mounting the board. Wrap a layer of Sellotape around the central region of the ferrite rod. On this wind about 85 turns of enamelled wire in a single layer, adjacent turns touching but not overlapping. Secure the ends of the coil with Sellotape. Bind the rod to the board with two loops of insulated wire, soldered in the holes at B13/B16 and W13/W16; pulling the wire tight while it is being soldered. Solder the ends of the coil to the two double-sided terminal pins above the board at Q12 and T12. Wires to VC1 are soldered to these pins below the board. Note that the wire from the pin at T12 goes to the 'earthy' side of the capacitor (i.e. the fixed plates). The plates of VC1 are below the board, with the bush passing up through the hole. A plastic knob is fixed to the spindle of VC1 above the board.

This radio receiver requires an amplifier module (see below). If you want to make a complete radio set, there is room on the right-hand end of the board for an amplifier circuit. The board can be mounted in a small plastic case or left unenclosed, supported on 4 'legs' made from 4 bolts about 25mm long.

Power requirements: 9V dc. 0.25mA.

Input specification: the radio requires a reasonably powerful local radio station. Reception of distant stations is better after dark.

Output specification: output is 4.5V, with a 60mV peak-to-peak audio signal superimposed on it. Reception is adequate with a 1-transistor amplifier and crystal earphone (Modules 27 and 59), but is far better with a 3-transistor amplifier and loudspeaker (Modules 28 and 62). You could also experiment with other amplifiers, such as one of the operational amplifier modules.

22 Sound Sensor

Function: to detect sounds, with an amplified output.

Circuit diagram: see Figure 47.

How it works: TR1 is biassed by R1 and R2 to be just turned on. A collector current of about 1mA flows through it. When sound reaches the piezo-electric crystal of the

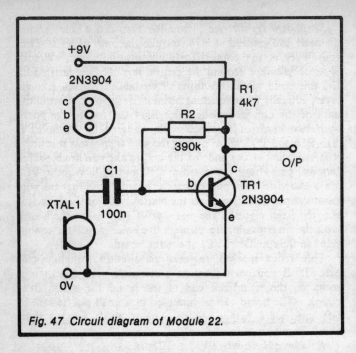

Fig. 47 Circuit diagram of Module 22.

microphone (XTAL1) small voltage changes are generated.
These signals are passed across C1 and, as the voltage rises and
falls, the base current increases and decreases. This causes a
corresponding increase and decrease in the collector current.
The transistor is connected in common-emitter mode, so that
there is considerable amplification of the voltage (see Module
27) and the collector current is far larger (over 100 times) the
current originating from the microphone, so providing more
power for driving an earphone or other amplifier modules.

Parts required: R1 4k7, R2 390k, C1 100n polyester layer,
TR1 2N3904 npn transistor, XTAL1 crystal microphone (a
cheap 'microphone insert' is usually good enough), 1mm
terminal pins (5 off), crocodile clips (2 off, red + blue).

Stripboard layout: wire links — J11 to O11, L5 to O5.
R1 — A11 to H11. R2 — H10 to I10. C1 — G8 to I8. TR1 —
H13(c), I13(b), J13(e). XTAL1 — G4 to L4. Terminal pins
— A1, A15, H15, O1, O15.

68

Power requirements: 9V dc. 1mA.

Input specification: voice at 10cm from the microphone. It is more sensitive to sharp high-pitched sounds, such as claps and whistles, as well as to sounds made by objects tapping on the surface on which the module is resting.

Output specification: 4.5V, with 50mA peak-to-peak audio signal superimposed.

Modifications: a second amplifier of this type (but without the microphone) can be connected to this, giving further amplification (2–3V peak-to-peak). The signal is badly distorted, so is unsuitable for audio applications, but can be used in intruder-detection and baby-alarm systems. Better audio quality is obtained by following this module with a 3-transistor amplifier (Module 28).

23 Voltage Reference

Function: to provide an accurate and stable voltage reference.

Circuit diagram: see Figure 48.

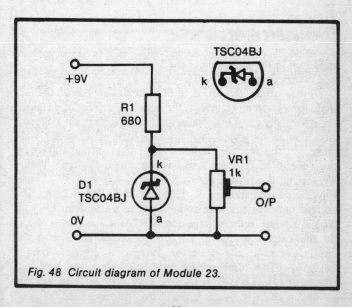

Fig. 48 Circuit diagram of Module 23.

69

How it works: D1 is a band-gap voltage reference, with a stable output of 1.26V. VR1 acts as a variable potential divider (see Module 9) to allow lower voltages to be obtained.

Parts required: R1 680, VR1 1k sub-miniature horizontal preset, D1 TSC04BJ band-gap voltage reference, 1mm terminal pins (5 off), crocodile clips (2 off, red + blue).

Stripboard layout: wire link — I7 to O7. R1 — A7 to G7. VR1 — G9, I9, and H13 (wiper), D1 — H5(k), I5(a). Terminal pins — A1, A15, H15, O1, O15. Cut strip beneath the board at H9. Solder blob joins G5 and H5.

Power requirements: 9V dc. 9mA.

Output specification: current drawn should not exceed 1mA.

Modifications: for a single-level source, omit VR1 and take the output directly from the junction of R1 and D1. With R1 as shown, V_{OUT} is constant for all currents up to a maximum current of 9mA. For other maximum currents (at least $15\mu A$, not more than 20mA) substitute other values for R1:

$$R1 = 7.74/I .$$

24 Constant Current Generator

Function: to produce a constant current, irrespective of variations in the resistance of the load.

Circuit diagram: see Figure 49.

How it works: the action of this circuit depends on the fact that, for a given base current, the collector current of a transistor is virtually constant. Variations in the load in the collector circuit or in the supply voltage have little effect over a wide range. In this module the base is held at a constant voltage by the Zener diode D1 and thus base current is constant. With a 9V supply, the voltage across R1 is $9 - 4.7 = 4.3V$. Therefore the current through R1 (the base current) is 4.3mA. The voltage between the base and emitter of a transistor (V_{be}) is 0.6V. Therefore the voltage across R2 is $4.7 - 0.6 = 4.1V$. So the current in R2 is $4.1/220 = 18.6mA$. This is the emitter current; the collector current is $18.6 - 4.3 = 14.3mA$. The total voltage dropped across the load and transistor (V_{ce}) is $9 - 4.1V = 4.8V$. If the load has low

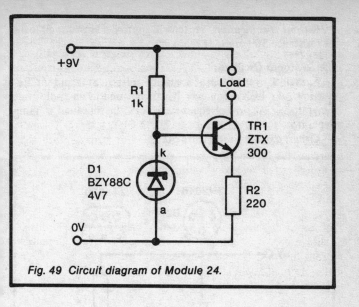

Fig. 49 Circuit diagram of Module 24.

resistance, the voltage dropped across the load is small and the greater part of the drop is across the transistor. With a larger load, there is a greater voltage drop across it and a correspondingly smaller drop across the transistor. The maximum allowable voltage drop across the load is 4.8V, corresponding to a resistance of 4.8/0.0143 = 330 ohms (approx.). Thus the circuit gives a constant current for all loads of 330 ohms or less.

Similarly, the supply voltage may be allowed to increase or decrease by a few volts without affecting the current through the load.

Parts required: R1 1k, R2 220, D1 BZY88C4V7, Zener diode 4.7V, TR1 ZTX300 npn transistor, 1mm terminal pins (5 off), crocodile clips (2 off, red + blue).

Stripboard layout: R1 — A5 to I5. R2 — J10 to O10. D1 — I7(k, banded end) to O7. TR1 — H12(c), I12(b), J12(e). Terminal pins — A1, A15, H15, O1, O15.

Power requirements: 9V dc. Approximately 20mA (4.3 mA plus the constant current.

71

Output specification: current is approx. 15mA for all loads of resistance 300 ohms or more.

25 Sawtooth Oscillator

Function: generates a sawtooth output at a pre-set frequency. At high frequency it can be used as an audio tone generator. At low frequency it can be used as a ramp generator.

Circuit diagram: see Figure 50.

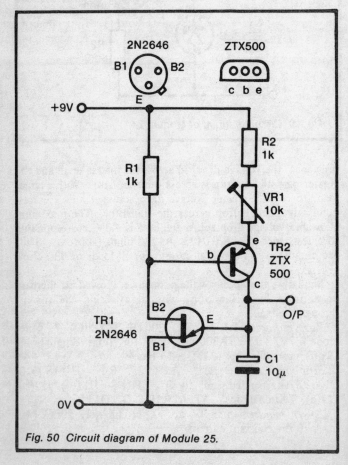

Fig. 50 Circuit diagram of Module 25.

How it works: TR1 is a unijunction transistor. TR2 together with R1, R2 and VR1, makes a constant current generator. Current flows through R2, VR1 and TR2 and gradually charges C1. When the voltage across C1 reaches a given value (the *peak point*, which is about 5 or 6V), current begins to flow into TR1 through the emitter and to the 0V rail by way of base 1. C1 is discharged rapidly, until the voltage across it has fallen to a lower value (the *valley point*, which is about 2V). The flow of current through the emitter then stops and C1 begins to charge again. Thus C1 charges slowly and discharges rapidly. The output of the circuit has a sawtooth waveform (Fig.51). Since the charging current

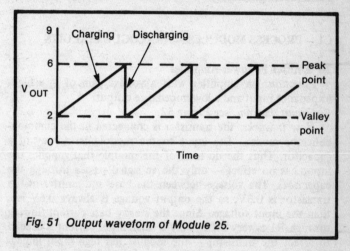

Fig. 51 Output waveform of Module 25.

comes from a constant current generator instead of simply through a resistor, the rate of increase of voltage across C1 is constant and the rising section of the waveform is a straight line, not a curve. An oscillator of this type, which works by switching a current on and off alternately, is known as a *relaxation oscillator* (compare with Module 17, which is a harmonic oscillator).

Parts required: R1, R2 1k (2 off), VR1 10k sub-miniature horizontal preset, C1, 10μ electrolytic, TR1 2N2646 unijunction transistor, TR2 ZTX500 pnp transistor, 1mm terminal pins (5 off), crocodile clips (2 off, red + blue).

Stripboard layout: wire link — I5 to O5. R1 — A4 to G4. R2 — A13 to D13. VR1 — D10, F10 and E6 (wiper). C1 — H10(+) to O10(−). TR1 — G6(B_2), H6(E), I6(B_1). TR2 — F13(e), G13(b), H13(c); this is a pnp transistor and the emitter is toward the *top* in Figure 50 and on the board. Terminal pins — A1, A15, H15, O1, O15. Solder blob joins E10 to F10.

Power requirements: 9V dc. 1.5mA.

Output specification: see Figure 51. Frequency range is 2Hz to 10Hz (suitable as ramp generator).

Modifications: if C1 is 10n, frequency range is 1kHz to 5kHz (audio generator).

C1 — PROCESS MODULES — ANALOGUE CIRCUITS

26 Emitter Follower Amplifier

Function: an amplifier with a voltage gain of 1, a high-impedance input and a low-impedance output.

Circuit diagram: see Figure 52.

How it works: the transistor is connected in the common-collector mode. The input to the module is by way of a capacitor. Thus the dc level of the module that supplies the input has no effect — only the ac signal passes through the capacitor. The voltage between the base and emitter of the transistor is 0.6V, so the output voltage is always 0.6V less than the input voltage. Since the steady base current flowing through R1 is very small, only a small input current is needed to affect the transistor — the module has high input impedance. Since the collector current is much larger than the base current (about 150 times, depending on the gain of the transistor) the module can supply a relatively large current to another module — the module has low output impedance. This amplifier is used for impedance matching. We may have a module with a high output impedance (i.e. is unable to supply a large current without an appreciable change in output voltage) — for example Module 22. We may wish to connect this to a module with low input impedance (i.e. requires a large current) — for example a loudspeaker,

74

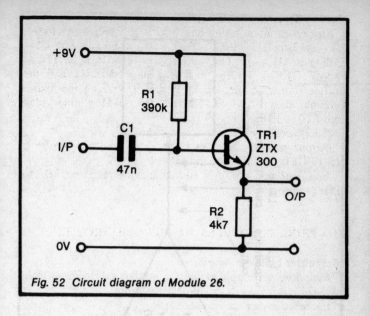

Fig. 52 *Circuit diagram of Module 26.*

Module 62. Module 22 is not able to supply enough current to drive a loudspeaker. Figure 53 shows how this module matches the impedances, allowing the signal from the microphone to produce sound in the loudspeaker. The additional power required comes from the current used by the emitter-follower circuit.

Parts required: R1 390k, R2 4k7, C1 47n polyester layer, TR1 ZTX300 npn transistor, 1mm terminal pins (6 off), crocodile clips (3 off, red + yellow + blue).

Stripboard layout: wire link − A7 to F7. R1 − A10 to G10. R2 − H10 to O10, C1 − G4 to J4. TR1 − F12(c), G12(b), and H12(e). Terminal pins − A1, A15, H15, I1, O1, O15. Solder blob joins I4 to J4.

Power requirements: 9V dc. 1mA.

Input specification: input impedance is 210k.

Output specification: output impedance is 39k in parallel with the output impedance of the module connected to the input, then divided by about 150. Current gain is given by h_{fe} for the transistor, which is approximately 150.

75

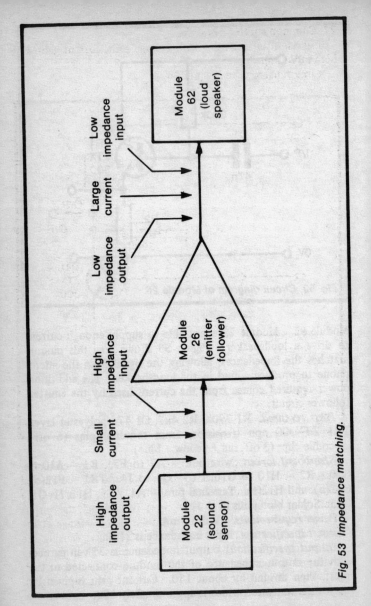

Fig. 53 Impedance matching.

76

27 Common-emitter Amplifier

Function: an amplifier with voltage gain, current gain, and high input impedance.

Circuit diagram: see Figure 54.

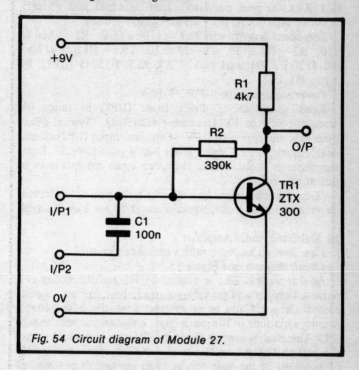

Fig. 54 Circuit diagram of Module 27.

How it works: the transistor is connected in common-emitter mode. It is biassed by a resistor R2 connected between its base and collector terminal. This improves the stability of the amplifier. When there is no signal, the output of the amplifier is about 3.5V. An increased voltage at the input causes an additional base current to flow, causing the current to increase. This results in an increased voltage being developed across R1. The effect is to lower the output voltage. Thus the output signal is the *inverse* of the input signal. The fact that the collector current is about 150 times greater than the base current means that a small change in base voltage brings about a relatively large change in collector voltage – there is voltage gain.

Parts required: R1 4k7, R2 390k, C1 100n polyester layer, TR1 ZTX300 npn transistor, 1mm terminal pins (7 off), crocodile clips (4 off, red + green + yellow + blue).

Stripboard layout: wire link – J10 to O10. R1 – A10 to H10. R2 – H8 to I8. C1 – I3 to L3. TR1 – H12(c), I12(b), and J12(e). Terminal pins – A1, A15, H15, I1 (I/P1), L1 (I/P2), O1, O15.

Power requirements: 9V dc. 1.5mA.

Input specification: direct input (I/P1) in range 0V (transistor off) to 9V (transistor saturated). Typical direct input is in the region of 0.7V. Capacitor input (I/P2) eliminates dc levels; typical signal levels 30mV peak-to-peak. Input impedance is about 400k. Only one input terminal is to be used at one time.

Output specification: current gain is the gain of the transistor (about 150). Voltage gain is about 70 for a small signal.

28 Stabilized Audio Amplifier

Function: an amplifier with variable gain control.

Circuit diagram: see Figure 55.

How it works: TR1 is biassed by R1 and R2, acting as a potential divider and providing a steady base current. Signals passed across C1 add to or subtract from this base current, causing variations in the much larger collector current through R3. The emitter current through VR1 also varies and causes the potential at the emitter to rise and fall. Since an increase of potential at the base results in an increase of potential at the emitter, there is negative feedback which opposes the effect of changes in base potential. This reduces the amount of amplification considerably. However, if VR1 is set so that C2 is connected to its upper end, C2 holds the emitter potential steady. The negative feedback effect is eliminated giving maximum amplification. C2 is said to *by-pass* the emitter resistor VR1. By varying the setting of VR1 so that the damping effect of C2 operates on part of VR1 but not on all of it, we can control the amount of feedback, and hence control the gain of the amplifier. VR1 acts as a *volume*

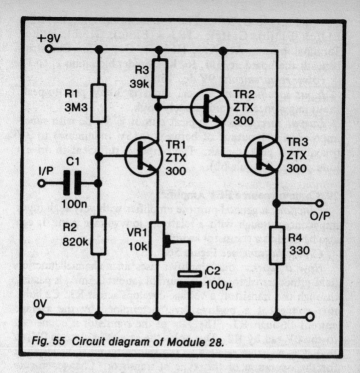

Fig. 55 Circuit diagram of Module 28.

control. The gain of this stage of the amplifier is thus independent of the gain of TR1 though, of course it is less than it would be in the absence of VR1.

The varying voltage at the collector of VR1 is fed to TR2 and TR3, which are connected as a Darlington pair (see Module 31) which gives very high current gain. The high and varying current passing through R4 produces large voltage changes at the emitter of TR3.

Parts required: R1 3M3, R2 820k, R3 39k, R4 330, VR1 10k sub-miniature horizontal preset, C1 100n polyester layer, C2 100μ electrolytic, 1mm terminal pins (6 off), crocodile clips (3 off, red + yellow + blue).

Stripboard layout: wire links – A12 to E12, I2 to K2, L6 to O6. R1 – A6 to H6. R2 – H5 to O5. R3 – A9 to F9. R4 – H14 to O14. VR1 – J7, L7 and K11 (wiper). C1 – H3 to K3.

C2 − K12(+) to O12(−). TR1 − F8(c), H8(b), I8(e). TR2 −
E11(c), F11(b), G11(e). TR3 − E13(c), G13(b), H13(e).
Terminal pins − A1, A15, H15, I1, O1, O15. Cut strips
beneath the board at H11, I6, K8. Solder blob joins I7 to J7.

Power requirements: 9V dc. 15mA.

Input specification: typical input is 30mV peak-to-peak.
Input impedance is approximately 680k.

Output specification: typical output is 5V dc with superimposed signal output of between 0.15V (minimum) to 3V
(maximum) peak-to-peak. The output is sufficient to drive a
loudspeaker (Module 62).

29 Common-source FET Amplifier

Function: a general-purpose amplifier with very high input
impedance, though with a relatively low voltage gain. It can
also be used as a transistor switch.

Circuit diagram: see Figure 56.

How it works: this amplifier uses an n-channel junction
field effect transistor. When current (about 0.5mA) is passing
through the transistor, a voltage develops across R3. C2 holds
this voltage at a positive level determined by the average
current through R3. The gate of the transistor is connected
to the 0V rail by R2. This holds the gate at or close to 0V, so
that it is negative relative to the source terminal, as required
for the operation of this type of transistor. Changes in gate
potential resulting from the input signal affect the amount of
current passing through the transistor from drain to source.
This varying current causes a varying voltage to appear across
R1, and thus an alternating signal voltage appears at O/P.

Parts required: R1 9k1, R2 1M, R3 5k6, C1 100n polyester
layer, C2 100μ electrolytic, TR1 2N3819 junction FET, 1mm
terminal pins (7 off), crocodile clips (4 off, red + yellow +
green + blue).

Stripboard layout: R1 − A10 to H10. R2 − I6 to O6.
R3 − J11 to O11. C1 − I4 to L4. C2 − J9(+) to O9(−). TR1
− H12(d), I12(g), J12(s). Terminal pins − A1, A15, H15, I1
(I/P1), L1(I/P2), O1, O15.

Power requirements: 9V dc. 0.5mA.

Input specification: I/P1 is intended for switching applications. I/P2 is for audio signals. No current flows to the gate

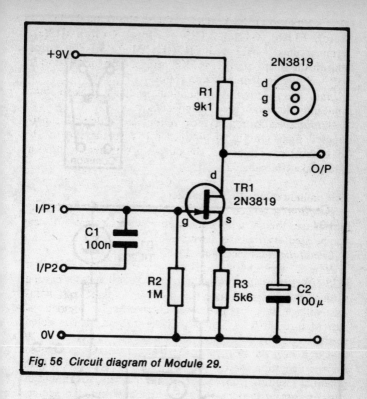

Fig. 56 Circuit diagram of Module 29.

of the FET, so the input impedance of the amplifier is the resistance of R2, which is 1M.

Output specification: Output is about 4.5V with no input signal. If an input signal of 60mV peak-to-peak is applied to I/P2, an output signal of about 200mV peak-to-peak is superimposed on this.

30 Schmitt Trigger

Function: converts a wavering input signal into a crisp, clear-cut output signal.

Circuit diagram: see Figure 57.

How it works: in this description, we assume that VR1 is set so that the full input voltage appears at its wiper, also that

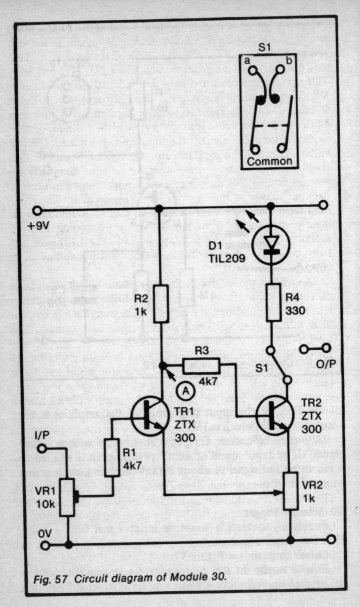

Fig. 57 Circuit diagram of Module 30.

82

S1 is switched as shown in the figure so that the LED is in the circuit. Suppose that the input is 0V. TR1 is off, so the voltage at point A is 9V. A base current flows from A to TR2, which is on. Current flows through the LED, TR2 and VR2. This current generates a voltage across VR2 and the wiper of VR2 is at a positive voltage, V. The emitter of VR1 is also at V volts. Now suppose the input voltage gradually increases. Nothing else happens until the base-emitter voltage of TR1 begins to exceed 0.6V, i.e. the input voltage reaches $(V + 0.6)$ volts. Then TR1 begins to turn on, current begins to flow through R2, and the voltage at point A falls. Gradually the base current to TR2 is reduced. As input voltage continues to rise, the voltage at the wiper of VR2 begins to fall. The effect of this is that the base-emitter voltage of TR1 increases *rapidly*, turning TR1 on rapidly and thus turning TR2 off rapidly. There is a sharp 'snap' action. The LED goes out. Now there is no current through VR2 and the voltage at its wiper has fallen to 0V.

Next suppose the input voltage begins to fall. There can be no change in the circuit until the base-emitter voltage becomes less than 0.6V. Since the emitter voltage of TR1 is 0V, the base voltage must fall below 0.6V before TR1 turns off. A small fall in input has no effect on the circuit. This is why slight fluctuations in the input voltage have no effect on the output of the circuit. However, once the input has fallen below 0.6V, TR1 is off, TR2 turns on (again there is a 'snap' action) and the LED lights. Now the wiper of VR2 is at V volts again. A slight rise in input has no effect because input must rise to $(V + 0.6)$ again before the TR1 can be turned on.

We thus have a circuit which changes state with a 'snap' action. A rising input causes it to change state at a voltage called the *upper threshold* voltage $(V + 0.6)$ and a falling input causes it to change state at the *lower threshold* voltage (0.6). The voltage V is known as the *hysteresis* of the circuit and can be set by adjusting VR2. The lower threshold can be set by adjusting VR1.

The module has an LED to indicate its state. It is also possible to switch the LED out of circuit if a logical output voltage is required.

Parts required: R1, R3 4k7 (2 off), R2 1k, R4 330, VR1

10k sub-miniature horizontal preset, VR2 1k sub-miniature horizontal preset, TR1, TR2 ZTX300 npn transistor (2 off), S1 SPDT single d.i.l. switch, 1mm terminal pins (6 off), crocodile clips (3 off, red + yellow + blue).

Stripboard layout: wire links – I2 to M2, F5 to K5, L14 to O14. R1 – E3 to N3. R2 – A6 to D6. R3 – D7 to I7. R4 – B15 to G15. VR1 – M5, O5, and N9 (wiper). VR2 – J10, L10, and K14 (wiper). D1 – A12(a) to B12(k). TR1 – D4(c), E4(b) and F4(e). TR2 – H8(c), I8(b), and J8(e). S1 – G14(a), H14(b) and G11/H11 (common). Terminal pins – A1, A15, H15, I1, O1, O15. Cut strips beneath the board at G12, H12, I4. Solder blob joins G11 to H11.

Power requirements: 9V dc. 1.5mA plus load (e.g. 15mA for the LED).

Input specification: depending on setting of VR1 and VR2:

Set VR1 to	Set VR2 to	Low threshold	Upper threshold	Hysteresis (V)
top	top	1.5	4.5	3.0
	middle	1.0	2.5	1.5
	bottom	0.6	0.6	nil*
middle	top	2.5	8.3	5.8
	middle	1.5	3.7	2.2
	bottom	1.0	1.0	nil*

*the Schmitt 'snap' action with hysteresis does not occur when the wiper of VR2 is turned to the 0V end. Higher inputs operate the circuit as the wiper of VR1 is turned toward its bottom end but, when the wiper is *at* the bottom end, it is permanently at 0V and no switching occurs.

Output specification: LED on or off. O/P high (9V) or low (0V) O/P is CMOS logic compatible. If the input is a sine wave, or a badly shaped (distorted) square wave, the output is a sharp square wave.

31 Darlington Pair

Function: an arrangement of transistors with very high current gain.

Circuit diagram: see Figure 58.

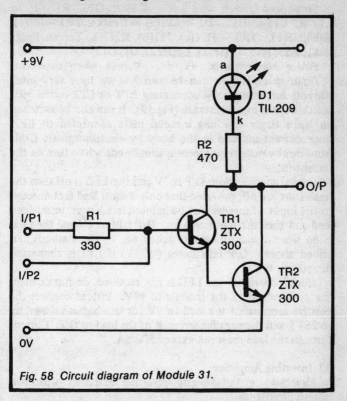

Fig. 58 Circuit diagram of Module 31.

How it works: suppose that the current gain of each transistor is 100. The collector current of TR1 becomes the base current of TR2, so the gain of the pair is 100 x 100, or 10000. The module has an LED to show whether the transistors are on or off, so the module can be used as an indicator. The output terminal allows it to be used as a very high gain amplifier, suitable for switching or for interfacing to logic circuits. The high gain makes it suitable for use as a touch switch.

Parts required: R1 330, R2 470, D1 TIL209 LED, TR1, TR2 ZTX300 npn transistor (2 off), 1mm terminal pins (7

85

off), crocodile clips (4 off, red + yellow + green + blue).

Stripboard layout: wire link − K13 to O13. R1 − I3 to L3. R2 C13 to H13. D1 − A11(a) to C11(k). TR1 − H8(c), I8(b), J8(e). TR2 − H11(c), J11(b), K11(e). Terminal pins − A1, A15, H15, I1 (IP/2), L1(I/P2), O1, O15.

Power requirements: 9V dc. 0.2mA when quiescent.

Input specification: can be switched on by a very small current, for example by connecting I/P1 or I/P2 to the +9V rail through a high resistance (Fig.59). It can also be switched on by a finger touching a metal plate connected to I/P2, since current induced in the body by electromagnetic fields from nearby mains equipment is usually enough to turn on the transistors.

Output specification: O/P is 7V and the LED is off then the transistors are off, provided that only a short lead is connected to the input. Currents may be induced in a longer, unshielded lead and turn the transistors on. O/P falls to 4V and the LED is on when transistors are switched on, by the methods described above. O/P falls lower (0.75V) if I/P1 is connected directly to +9V.

Modifications: if the LED is not required, do not connect the positive rail of the module to +9V. Instead connect the positive terminal of the load to 9V (or to a higher voltage, up to 25V), and the negative terminal of the load to O/P. Current through the load must not exceed 500mA.

32 Inverting Amplifier

Function: a variable-gain inverting amplifier with low output impedance.

Circuit diagram: see Figure 60.

How it works: this is based on a CMOS operational amplifier ic. It has two inputs to allow for either dc input (I/P1) or ac input (I/P2). Input goes to the inverting input (−) of the amplifier while the non-inverting input (+) is held at 0V. The output of the amplifier is fed back to the inverting input, by way of VR1 and R2. The output of the amplifier (measured relative to the 0V rail) depend on the *difference* of the voltages at its inputs. If the input at (−) is positive, the output swings negative, until the (−) terminal is at 0V, the same as the (+) terminal. This is shown in Figure 61. The input

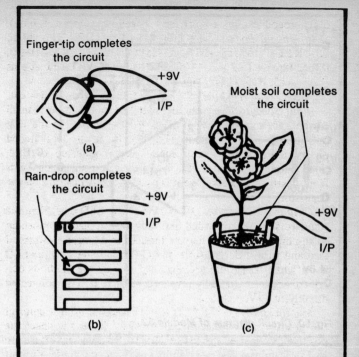

Fig. 59 High-resistance "switches" for Module 31.
(a) Touch-plate made of two metal plates with a gap between them.
(b) Rain-detector plate etched on a piece of copper-clad circuit board.
(c) Soil moisture detection, in which the circuit is broken when the soil becomes dry.

current flows along R1, past the (−) input, which is at 0V, through R2 and VR1 and *into* the output terminal of the amplifier. Let the combined resistance of R2 and VR1, the feedback resistors, be R_F. For R1, the current I is $V_{IN}/R1$. For R2 and VR1, the current I is $-V_{OUT}/R_F$. It is a negative current since it is flowing *away from* a point at 0V. Since I is the same for both parts of the circuit:

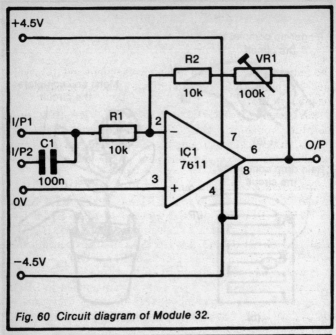

Fig. 60 Circuit diagram of Module 32.

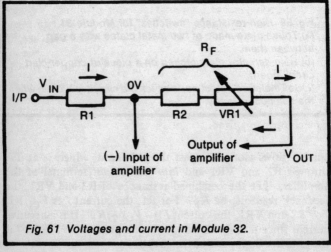

Fig. 61 Voltages and current in Module 32.

$$V_{IN}/R1 = -V_{OUT}/R_F$$

and
$$V_{OUT} = -V_{IN} \times R_F/R1$$

The output is inverted with respect to the input and its magnitude is determined by the ratio of the feedback resistor(s) to the input resistor.

Parts required: R1, R2 10k (2 off), VR1 100k subminiature horizontal preset, C1 100n polyester layer, IC1 7611 CMOS operational amplifier, 8-pin d.i.l. socket, 1mm terminal pins (9 off), crocodile clips (5 off, red + yellow + green + blue + black).

Stripboard layout: wire links — A13 to G13, D12 to H12, F11 to P11, H5 to O5, I6 to P6. R1 — G2 to I2. R2 — B5 to G5. VR1 — B11, D11, and C7 (wiper), C1 — I3 to L3. IC1 — F7(pin 1) to I10(pin 5). Terminal pins — A1, A15, H15, I1 (I/P1), L1 (I/P2), O1, O15, P1, P15. Cut strips beneath the board at I4, F8 to I8. Solder blob joins B11 to C11.

Power requirements: 9V dc. Less than 1mA.

Input specification: dc signals (±4.5V are applied to I/P1); ac signals (e.g. from radio Module 21) are coupled by capacitor C1, via I/P2. Input impedance is 10k (the value of R1).

Output specification: output voltage can be up to ±4.5V, and output impedance is only a few tens of ohms. Voltage gain depends on the setting of VR1. With VR1 set to zero, feedback resistance is 10k so gain is −1. With VR1 set to 100k, feedback resistance is 110k, so gain is −11.

Modifications: other values of R2 and VR1 can be substituted to give a different range of gains. Or a single fixed resistor can be used to give a fixed gain. For example, if R_F is 1M, gain is 100. Use 1% tolerance resistors (or better) if precision is important.

33 Non-inverting Amplifier

Function: a variable-gain non-inverting amplifier with very high input impedance and low output impedance.

Circuit diagram: see Figure 62.

How it works: this is based on a CMOS operational amplifier ic. It has two inputs to allow for either dc input (I/P1) or ac input (I/P2). Input goes to the non-inverting input (+) of

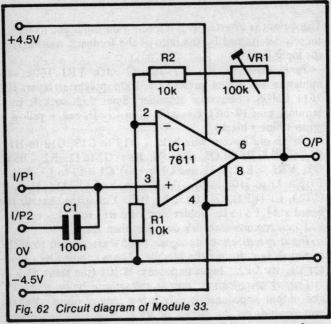

Fig. 62 Circuit diagram of Module 33.

the amplifier while the inverting input (−) is connected to a
resistor chain. The output of the amplifier is fed back to the
inverting input by way of this chain. The output of the
amplifier depends on the *difference* of the voltages at its
inputs. If the input at (+) is positive, the output swings
positive, until the (−) terminal is at the same potential as the
(+) terminal. Let the combined resistance of R2 and VR1,
the feedback resistors, be R_F. The current flowing along
VR1, R2 and R1 is $I = V_{OUT}/(R1 + R_F)$. The (−) terminal
is V_{IN} so, for R1 alone, $I = V_{IN}/R1$. Since I is the same for
both equations:

$$V_{IN}/R1 = V_{OUT}/(R1 + R_F)$$

and $$V_{OUT} = V_{IN} \times (R1 + R_F)/R1$$

90

The output has the same polarity as the input and its magnitude is determined by the ratio of the feedback resistor(s) to the input resistor.

Parts required: R1, R2 10k (2 off), VR1 100k subminiature horizontal preset, C1 100n polyester layer, IC1 7611 CMOS operational amplifier, 8-pin d.i.l. socket, 1mm terminal pins (9 off), crocodile clips (5 off, red + yellow + green + blue + black).

Stripboard layout: wire links — A13 to G13, D12 to H12, F11 to P11, I6 to P6. R1 — G5 to O5. R2 — B3 to G3. VR1 — B11, D11, and C7 (wiper). C1 — I3 to L3. IC1 — F7(pin 1) to I10(pin 5). Terminal pins — A1, A15, H15, I1 (I/P1, L1(I/P2), O1, O15, P1, P15. Cut strips beneath the board at I4, F8 to I8. Solder blobs join B11 to C11, H2 to I2.

Power requirements: 9V dc. Less than 1mA.

Input specification: dc signals (±4.5V are applied to I/P1); ac signals (e.g. from radio Module 21) are coupled by capacitor C1, via I/P2. Input impedance is 10^{12} ohms, the input impedance of the non-inverting input of the ic.

Output specification: output voltage can be up to ±4.5V, and output impedance is only a few tens of ohms. Voltage gain depends on the setting of VR1. With VR1 set to zero, feedback resistance is 10k so gain is 2. With VR1 set to 100k, feedback resistance is 110k, so gain is 12.

Modifications: other values of R2 and VR1 can be substituted to give a different range of gains. Or a single fixed resistor can be used to give a fixed gain. For example, if R_F is 1M, gain is 101. Use 1% tolerance resistors (or better) if precision is important.

34 Voltage Follower

Function: a non-inverting amplifier with unity gain, a very high input impedance and very low low output impedance. Used for impedance matching (see Fig.53).

Circuit diagram: see Figure 63.

How it works: this is based on a CMOS operational amplifier ic. It has two inputs to allow for either dc input (I/P1) or ac input (I/P2). Input goes to the non-inverting input (+) of the amplifier. The output of the amplifier is fed back to the inverting input. If the input at (+) is positive, the output

91

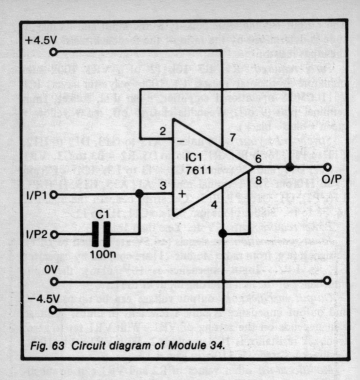

Fig. 63 Circuit diagram of Module 34.

swings positive, until the (−) terminal is at the same potential as the (+) terminal. Similarly, if the input is negative. Thus the output has the same polarity and magnitude as the input:

$$V_{OUT} = V_{IN}$$

Parts required: C1 100n polyester layer, IC1 7611 CMOS operational amplifier, 8-pin d.i.l. socket, 1mm terminal pins (9 off), crocodile clips (5 off, red + yellow + green + blue + black).

Stripboard layout: wire links − A13 to G13, G4 to H12, F11 to P11, I6 to P6. C1 − I3 to L3. IC1 − F7(pin 1) to I10(pin 5). Terminal pins − A1, A15, H15, I1 (I/P1), L1 (I/P2), O1, O15, P1, P15. Cut strips beneath the board at I4, F8 to I8. Solder blob joins H2 to I2.

Power requirements: 9V dc. Less than 1mA.

Input specification: dc signals (±4.5V are applied to I/P1); ac signals (e.g. from radio Module 21) are coupled by capacitor C1, via I/P2. Input impedance is 10^{12} ohms, the input impedance of the non-inverting input of the ic.

Output specification: output voltage can be up to ±4.5V, and output impedance is only a few tens of ohms. Voltage gain is 1.

35 Differential Amplifier

Function: an amplifier the output of which is proportional to the difference between its inputs. This type of amplifier is also known as a *subtractor*.

Circuit diagram: see Figure 64.

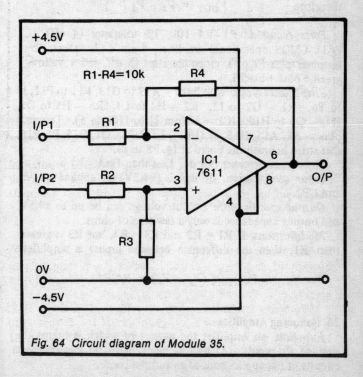

Fig. 64 Circuit diagram of Module 35.

How it works: this is based on a CMOS operational amplifier ic. All four resistors are equal; let us say their resistance is R. If the input at I/P2 is V_2, then the voltage at the (+) terminal is $V_2/2$, since R2 = R3. The output of the amplifier changes until the voltage at the (−) terminal is also $V_2/2$. The input at I/P1 is V_1. The current flowing through R1 is then $(V_1 - V_2/2)/R$. The current flowing along R4 is $(V_2/2 - V_{OUT})/R$. The two currents are equal, since no current can flow into or out of the (−) terminal. Thus:

$$(V_1 - V_2/2)/R = (V_2/2 - V_{OUT})/R$$

so

$$V_1 - V_2/2 = V_2/2 - V_{OUT}$$

therefore

$$V_{OUT} = V_2 - V_1$$

Parts required: R1−R4 10k, 1% tolerance (4 off), IC1 7611 CMOS operational amplifier, 8-pin d.i.l. socket, 1mm terminal pins (9 off), crocodile clips (5 off, red + yellow + green + blue + black).

Stripboard layout: wire links − A13 to G13, F11 to P11, I6 to P6. R1 − G2 to I2. R2 − H4 to L4. R3 − H5 to O5. R4 − G6 to H12. IC1 − F7(pin 1) to I10(pin 5). Terminal pins − A1, A15, H15, I1 (I/P1), L1 (I/P2), O1, O15, P1, P15. Cut strips beneath the board at I4, F8 to I8.

Power requirements: 9V dc. Less than 1mA.

Input specification: dc signals (±4.5V) are applied to I/P1 and I/P2.

Output specification: output voltage can be up to ±4.5V, and output impedance is only a few tens of ohms.

Modifications: if R1 = R2 and R3 = R4, but R3 is greater than R1, then the difference between inputs is amplified:

$$V_{OUT} = (V_2 - V_1) \times R4/R1$$

36 Summing Amplifier

Function: an amplifier the output of which is minus the sum of its inputs. As well as being useful in measurement circuits, it has applications as an audio mixer.

Circuit diagram: see Figure 65.

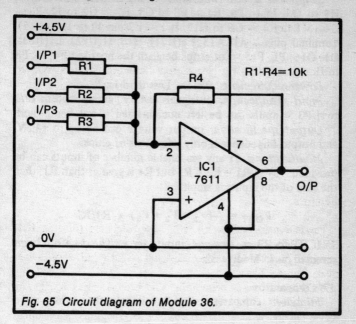

Fig. 65 Circuit diagram of Module 36.

How it works: this is based on a CMOS operational amplifier ic. All four resistors are equal; let us say their resistance is R. The (+) input is at 0V, so the amplifier output will be such that the (−) input is also 0V. Whatever currents flow through R1, R2 and R3 toward the (−) input, a single current equal to their total flows through R4 to the output terminal.

$$V_{\text{OUT}} = -(V_1 + V_2 + V_3).$$

Since the (−) input is always at 0V, it functions as a *virtual earth.* Current flowing in through any one of the resistors R1 to R3 is unaffected by current flowing in through any others.

Parts required: R1–R4 10k, 1% tolerance (4 off), IC1 7611 CMOS operational amplifier, 8-pin d.i.l. socket, 1mm terminal pins (10 off), crocodile clips (6 off, red + yellow + green + white + blue + black).

95

Stripboard layout: wire links – A13 to G13, F11 to P11, H5 to O5. I6 to P6. R1 – F3 to G3. R2 – G2 to I2. R3 – G4 to L4. R4 – G6 to H12. IC1 – F7(pin 1) to I10(pin 5). Terminal pins – A1, A15, F1(IP/1), H15, I1(I/P2), L1(I/P3), O1, O15, P1, P15. Cut strips beneath the board at F4, I4, F8 to I8.

Power requirements: 9V dc. Less than 1mA.

Input specification: dc signals (±4.5V) are applied to IP/1 to I/P3. Inputs can be left unconnected if not being used.

Output specification: output voltage can be up to ±4.5V, and output impedance is only a few tens of ohms.

Modifications: 1) any reasonable number of inputs can be provided. 2) If R1 = R2 = R3 but R4 is greater than R1, then the sum of the inputs is amplified:

$$V_{OUT} = -(V_1 + V_2 + V_3) \times R4/R1$$

3) If R1 to R3 are *unequal*, inputs are *weighted* before being summed, as in Module 52.

37 Comparator

Function: compares its input voltage with a preset reference voltage.

Circuit diagram: see Figure 66.

How it works: this is based on an LM311 comparator ic. The reference voltage V_{REF} is provided by VR1, acting as a potential divider (see Module 9). If the input is greater than V_{REF}, the output of the comparator swings sharply toward +4.5V. If the input is less than V_{REF}, the output is 0V. Note: unlike the output of operational amplifiers, the comparator output does *not* swing negative of the 0V rail (see *Modifications*, below).

Parts required: R1 1k, VR1 10k sub-miniature horizontal preset, IC1 LM311 comparator, 8-pin d.i.l. socket, 1mm terminal pins (8 off), crocodile clips (4 off, red + yellow + green + blue).

Stripboard layout: wire links – A3 to L3, A11 to G11, G2 to O2, I5 to M5, J6 to P6, N7 to P7. R1 – A12 to H12. VR1 – L10, N10, M14 (wiper). IC1 – G7(pin 1) to J10(pin 5). Terminal pins – A1, A15, H15, I1, O1, O15, P1, P15. Cut strips beneath the board at I4, G8 to J8. Solder blob joins H3 to I3.

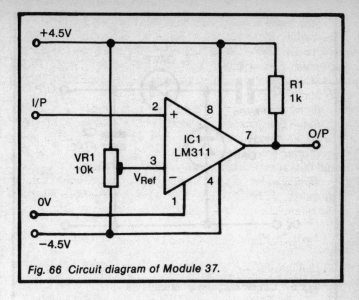

Fig. 66 Circuit diagram of Module 37.

Power requirements: 9V dc. Less than 1mA.

Input specification: dc signals (+4.5V). Adjust VR1 to set the reference voltage between +4.5V and −4.5V. Input impedance varies as the output changes, so the input should, if possible, be fed from a low impedance source.

Output specification: output voltage from 0V to +4.5V. This is *not* compatible with CMOS logic operating on 9V. If logic compatibility is required, operate the module on ±9V. Then the output is 0V (low) or +9V (high).

38 Diode Pump

Function: to produce a gradually increasing output whenever it receives an alternating input signal. An application of this appears on p.161.

Circuit diagram: see Figure 67.

How it works: the device has a capacitor on its input side, which accepts an alternating input signal irrespective of its dc level. As the input voltage rises above 0V, current flows through the D2 and increases the charge on C2. As the input voltage falls below 0V, D2 prevents the capacitor from losing

97

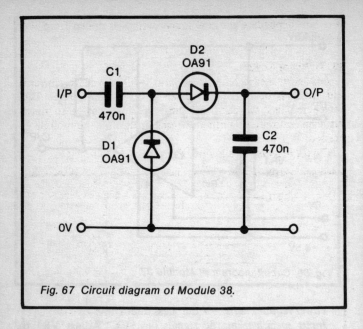

Fig. 67 Circuit diagram of Module 38.

charge. Current flows from the 0V rail to keep the diode
side of C1 at 0V. Each time the input signal goes positive,
additional charge is accumulated on C2. Gradually the charge
of C2 rises. The greater the frequency and the ·greater the
amplitude of the input signal, the higher the charge obtained.
Germanium diodes are used in this module as they have a
forward voltage drop of only 0.2V. This minimises the effect
of forward voltage drop on the output voltage.

Parts required: C1, C2 470n polyester layer (2 off), D1, D2
OA91 germanium point contact diode (2 off), 1mm terminal
pins (4 off), crocodile clips (2 off, yellow + blue).

Stripboard layout: wire link – K10 to O10. C1 – F4 to
I4. C2 – H12 to K12. D1 – F7(band) to O7. D2 – F10 to
H10(band). Terminal pins – H15, I1, O1, O15.

Power requirements: none.

Input specification: alternating voltage.

Output specification: voltage increasing from 0V to twice
the maximum input voltage. Falls when input signal ceases,

at a rate depending on how much current is drawn from the output.

39 Thyristor Switch

Function: a switching circuit which will pass a large current and which is operated by a small positive-going pulse. The device remains switched on until the load ceases to draw sufficient current or until the reset button on the module is pressed.

Circuit diagram: see Figure 68.

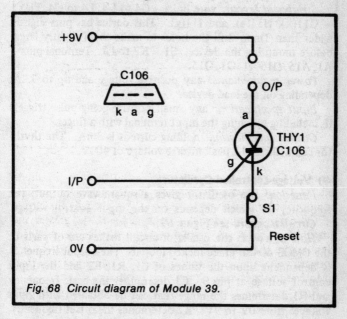

Fig. 68 Circuit diagram of Module 39.

How it works: the thyristor, on which this module is based, has the property that it conducts in only one direction. Its symbol is like that of a diode to indicate this. However, the device does not conduct, even in the forward direction, until it has been triggered by a positive-going pulse at its gate terminal. Current then flows through the load and the device but ceases when the amount of current falls below a critical value, known as the *holding current*. At that point, the device becomes non-conducting again, and remains non-conducting until it is re-triggered.

Parts required: THY1 C106 thyristor, S1 push-to-break push-button; a pcb-mounting push-to-*break* button does not seem to be available. Alternatives are (1) fit a panel-mounting button; (2) use a SPST d.i.l. switch instead. 1mm terminal pins (6 off), crocodile clips (3 off, red + yellow + blue), a bolt-on heat sink may be required if the thyristor is to carry large currents for prolonged periods.

Stripboard layout: wire links — G4 to K4, L4 to O4. THY1 — G11(k), H11(a), and I11(g). This device has pins slightly wider than 1mm; drill the holes to make them slightly larger before mounting the device. S1 — K7 to L7. Terminal pins — A1, A15, H15, I1, O1, O15.

Power requirements: any positive voltage and up to 3.2A, depending on the load device.

Input specification: any small positive-going pulse triggers it, including touching the input terminal with a finger.

Output specification: holding current is 3mA. The thyristor can withstand a peak inverse voltage of 400V.

40 Voltage-controlled Oscillator

Function: the oscillator gives a square-wave output, the frequency of which depends on the input control voltage.

Circuit diagram: see Figure 69.

How it works: the oscillator circuit makes use of parts of the CMOS 4046B phase locked loop ic. The output frequency is dependent upon the values of C1, R1, R2 and the input control voltage at pin 9. C1 determines the basic frequency and R1 determines the range that can be obtained with input voltages from 0V to 9V. R2 determines the offset frequency, the frequency obtained when input is 0V.

The minimum frequency of the VCO, produced when V_{IN} is 0V, is given by:

$$f = 1/R2.C1$$

The maximum frequency of the VCO, produced when V_{IN} is 9V, is given by:

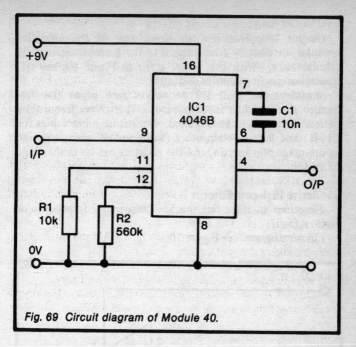

Fig. 69 Circuit diagram of Module 40.

$$f = 1/R1.C1 + \text{min. frequency}.$$

In both equations, C1 is expressed in farads.

Parts required: R1 10k, R2 560k, C1 10n polyester layer, IC1 4046B CMOS phase locked loop ic, 16-pin d.i.l. socket, 1mm terminal pins (6 off), crocodile clips (3 off, red + yellow + blue).

Stripboard layout: wire links — A6 to K6, C14 to E14, D2 to I2, D11 to O11. R1 — F4 to O4. R2 — G5 to O5. C1 — C12 to F12. IC1 — K10(pin 1) to D7(pin 9). This ic is mounted 'upside down', pin 1 at bottom right. Terminal pins — A1, A15, H15, I1, O1, O15. Cut strips beneath the board at D8 to K8, I3.

Power requirements: 9V dc. 0.2mA to 2.3mA, the higher the frequency the greater the current.

Input specification: voltage in the range 0 to 9V. Input from a potential divider allows tone to be varied in pitch. Inputs from slow square-wave, sine-wave or sawtooth generators give

101

a variety of siren and warbling effects.

Output specification: can drive any of the amplifier modules, or directly feed a signal to the loudspeaker module (Module 62). With the values given in Figure 69, the frequency ranges from 200Hz to 10kHz.

Modifications: omit R2 to obtain zero offset (i.e. frequency is zero when input is zero). This allows frequencies of less than 1Hz to be obtained. Substitute other values for C1, R1 and R2 to obtain other ranges and offsets. C1 can be in the range 50p to 10n, and the resistors can be in the range 5k to 1M.

41 Active High-pass Filter

Function: to filter out the low-frequency components of audio signals.

Circuit diagram: see Figure 70.

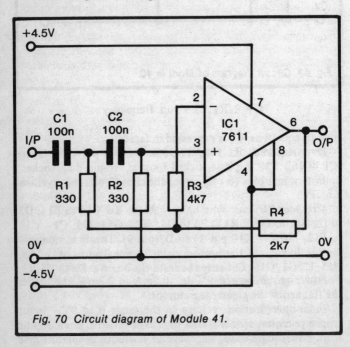

Fig. 70 Circuit diagram of Module 41.

How it works: this active filter, or *tuned amplifier*, is based on an operational amplifier. The filter has a two-section high-pass network (C1, C2, R1 and R2). High-frequency signals are readily passed across the capacitors to the amplifier, since capacitors behave as if they have a very low resistance to high frequencies. But low frequencies are not readily passed to the amplifier. This is because, at low frequencies, a capacitor behaves as if it has a very high resistance — in the extreme, at zero frequency, the capacitor has the very high resistance of its dielectric layer. The output from the amplifier (consisting mainly of high frequencies) is fed back to the first stage of the network through R1. This effect opposes high frequency signals passed out of the network through R1, and thus the high frequency signals are more strongly routed to the amplifier, increasing the filter effect. The signal also goes to the (−) input, making the effect of the signal to the (+) input relatively stronger and further increasing the filtering effect. As a result, the active filter features very sharp cut-off of frequencies below the selected frequency, far sharper than can be obtained by several stages of capacitors and resistors, or by using inductors (coils wound on iron cores) with their disadvantages of size and weight.

The cut-off frequency is given by:

$$f_c = 1/2\pi RC$$

where *R* is the value of R1 and R2, and *C* is the value of C1 and C2.

Parts required: R1, R2 330 (2 off), R3 4k7, R4 2k7, C1, C2 100n polyester layer (2 off), IC1 7611 CMOS operational amplifier, 8-pin d.i.l. socket, 1mm terminal pins (8 off), crocodile clips (4 off, red + yellow + blue + black).

Stripboard layout: wire links — A13 to G13, F14 to P14, I5 to P5. R1 — E3 to K3. R2 — H6 to O6. R3 — G7 to K7. R4 — H12 to K12. C1 — E2 to H2. C2 — E5 to H5. IC1 — F8(pin 1) to I11(pin 5). Terminal pins — A1, A15, H15, I1, O1, O15, P1, P15. Cut strips beneath the board at F9 to I9, H4, I4. Solder blob joins H2 to I2.

Power requirements: ±4.5V dc, less than 1mA.

Input specification: accepts audio outputs, for example

from the radio module followed by an amplifier.

Output specification: can drive the loudspeaker module (Module 62). With components shown the cut-off frequency is 5kHz. Frequencies below this are considerably reduced in power.

Modifications: other values for R1, R2, C1 and C2 can be used to give other cut-off frequencies.

42 Active Low-pass Filter

Function: to filter out the high-frequency components of audio signals.

Circuit diagram: see Figure 71.

How it works: this active filter, or *tuned amplifier*, is based on an operational amplifier. The filter has a two-section low-pass network (C1, C2, R1 and R2). High-frequency signals are readily passed across the capacitors to the 0V rail and the feedback loop and thus do not reach the inputs of the amplifier. Low frequencies pass through the resistors to the amplifier (+) input. The output from the amplifier (consisting mainly of low frequencies) is fed back to the first stage of the network, through C1. This effect opposes low frequency signals passing out of the network through C1, and thus the signals are more strongly routed to the amplifier, increasing the filter effect. The signal also goes to the (−) input, making the effect of the signal to the (+) input relatively stronger and further increasing the filtering effect. As a result, the active filter features very sharp cut-off of frequencies above the selected frequency, far sharper than can be obtained by several stages of capacitors and resistors or by using inductors.

The cut-off frequency is given by:

$$f_c = 1/2\pi RC$$

where R is the value of R1 and R2, and C is the value of C1 and C2.

Parts required: R1, R2 6k8 (2 off), R3 4k7, R4 2k7, C1, C2 100n polyester layer (2 off), IC1 7611 CMOS operational amplifier, 8-pin d.i.l. socket, 1mm terminal pins (8 off), crocodile clips (4 off, red + yellow + blue + black).

Stripboard layout: wire links — A13 to G13, F14 to P14,

104

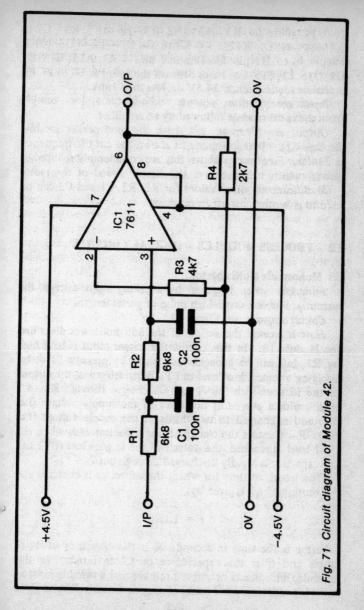

Fig. 71 Circuit diagram of Module 42.

I6 to P6, H4 to L4. R1 − I2 to N2. R2 − H5 to N5. R3 − G7 to K7. R4 − H12 to K12. C1 − K9 to N9. C2 − L3 to O3. IC1 − F8(pin 1) to I11(pin 5). Terminal pins − A1, A15, H15, I1, O1, O15, P1, P15. Cut strips beneath the board at F9 to I9, I3.

Power requirements: ±4.5V dc, less than 1mA.

Input specification: accepts audio outputs, for example from the radio module followed by an amplifier.

Output specification: can drive the loudspeaker module (Module 62). With components shown the cut-off frequency is 234Hz. Frequencies above this are considerably reduced in power, which helps remove the 'tinny' sound of the radio.

Modifications: other values for R1, R2, C1 and C2 can be used to give other cut-off frequencies.

C2 − PROCESS MODULES − DIGITAL CIRCUITS

43 Monostable Multivibrator

Function: when triggered by a falling input voltage, the output produces a single high pulse of preset length.

Circuit diagram: see Figure 72.

How it works: the action of the 555 timer was described for Module 18. In this circuit the trigger input is held high by R2, but can be brought low, either by pressing S1 or by applying a logical low level to I/P. When triggered, the output of the IC goes high (+9V) and C1 charges through R1. C1 begins with a charge of one-third of the supply voltage (i.e. 3V) and is charged to two-thirds of the supply voltage (i.e. 6V). Pin 6 senses the charge on the capacitor and, when the final level is reached, the output of the ic goes low (0V) and the capacitor is rapidly discharged through pin 7.

The length of time for which the capacitor is charging and for output is high is given by:

$$t = 1.1RC$$

where t is the time in seconds, R is the resistance of R1 in ohms and C is the capacitance of C1 in farads. In this module, R1 consists of a fixed resistor and a variable resistor, allowing resistance, and hence timing, to be varied over a given

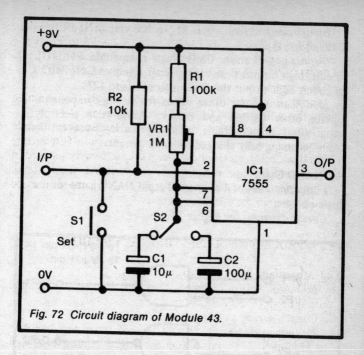

Fig. 72 Circuit diagram of Module 43.

range. There are two capacitors which can be switched in giving two timing ranges.

Parts required: R1 100k, R2 10k, VR1 1M sub-miniature horizontal preset, C1 10μ electrolytic, C2 100μ electrolytic, IC1 7555 timer ic, S1 push-to-make push-button (as in Fig. 21), S2 SPST d.i.l. switch, 8-pin d.i.l. socket, 1mm terminal pins (6 off), crocodile clips (3 off, red + yellow + blue).

Stripboard layout: wire links — A2 to E2, B1 to O2, C1 to I2, D3 to H4, D14 to F14, F8 to I9, G9 to I12, I6 to M6. R1 — A14 to B14. R2 — E3 to I3. VR1 — B13, D13, and C9(wiper). C1 — I8(+) to O8. C2 — I13(+) to O13. IC1 — B4(pin 1) to E7 (pin 5). S1 — M3/M5 to O3/O5. S2 — F10, G10, and F13/G13 (common, see Fig.57). Terminal pins — A1, A15, H15, I1, O1, O15. Cut strips beneath the board at B5 to E5, B9, F11, G11, I7, I10. Solder blobs join A7 to B7, C7 to D7, F13 to G13.

Power requirements: 9V dc. Negligible current when quiescent, can source or sink up to 100mA.

Input specification: press S1, reduce voltage at I/P, or use CMOS logic input.

Output specification: CMOS logic compatible. With C1 in circuit, high output time ranges from 1.1s to 12.1s. With C2 in circuit high output time ranges from 11s to 121s.

Modifications: use other values for timing components to obtain other timings and ranges. Large-value electrolytic capacitors are not suitable, as leakage currents prevent them from becoming fully charged by small currents.

44 NAND Gates

Function: a set of 4 separate 2-input NAND gates for use in logic circuits.

Circuit diagram: see Figure 73.

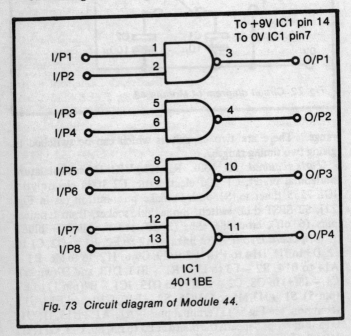

Fig. 73 Circuit diagram of Module 44.

How it works: In CMOS logic that is operating on a 9V supply, the following input and output voltages apply:

	Logic low ('0')	Logic high ('1')
Input	0 – 3.5V	6.5 – 9V
Output	less than 0.05V	more than 8.95V

The action of a NAND gate is shown by this truth table:

Inputs		Output
A	B	Z
0	0	1
0	1	1
1	0	1
1	1	0

In this table, '0' and '1' represent low and high inputs or outputs respectively, as defined in the previous table.

Parts required: IC1 4011BE quadruple 2-input NAND gate, 14-pin d.i.l. socket, 1mm terminal pins (16 off), crocodile clips (10 off, red + 4 yellow + 4 green + blue).

Stripboard layout: it is not necessary to implement or to use all four logic gates but it is a rule with CMOS that inputs must not be left to 'float' If any gates are not implemented or are unused, their input *must* be connected to the +9V or 0V rails. Wire links – A10 to D10, F3 to H4, G3 to I4, H2 to J10, I2 to I10, J2 to F10, K2 to E10, F5 to D14, G5 to F14, G10 to J14, J5 to O5. IC1 – D6(pin 1) to J9(pin 8). Terminal pins – A1, A15, H15, O1, O15, and the following:

Gate No.	Inputs	Outputs
1	D1/E1	D15
2	F1/G1	F15
3	H1/I1	H15
4	J1/K1	J15

Cut strips beneath the board at D7 to J7, F4, G4, H3 to K3, D12, F12, J12.

Power requirements: 9V dc, and negligible current.

Input specification: see *How it works*, above.

Output specification: see *How it works*, above.

Modifications: substitute other quadruple-gate ics with the same gate layout. Truth tables of suitable ics are:

4001BE (NOR)			4030BE (exclusive-OR)		
Inputs		Output	Inputs		Output
A	B	Z	A	B	Z
0	0	1	0	0	0
0	1	0	0	1	1
1	0	0	1	0	1
1	1	0	1	1	0

45 Bistable Flip-flop

Function: a simple 'memory' circuit that gives a high or a low output, depending on which of its two inputs was last made low.

Circuit diagram: see Figure 74.

How it works: the bistable consists of two cross-connected NAND gates. Both of the inputs are normally high, and, in this module, held high by pull-up resistors R1 and R2. The circuit is stable in either of two states. In the set state, the output of gate 1 (pin 3) is high, and that of gate 2 (pin 4) is low. Pin 2 receives a low input from gate 2. As a result of this making I/P1 (SET) low has no effect (see truth table for NAND, Module 44). Pin 5 receives a high input from gate 1, so a low input to I/P2 (RESET), make the output of gate 2 go high. This makes both inputs of gate 1 high, so its output goes low. The low output from gate 1 goes to pin 5, so both inputs to that gate are now low, but this does not affect its output, which is already high. Now the low input at I/P2 can be made high again, and the output of gate 2 remains high. The bistable is now at its reset state. Further low levels applied to I/P2 have no effect, but a low to I/P1 makes the bistable change back to its set state. We leave it to the reader to work out how this happens.

Summing up, the circuit is triggered by a low pulse to either the set or reset inputs. The corresponding output (O/P1 or O/P2) goes high, and the other output goes low.

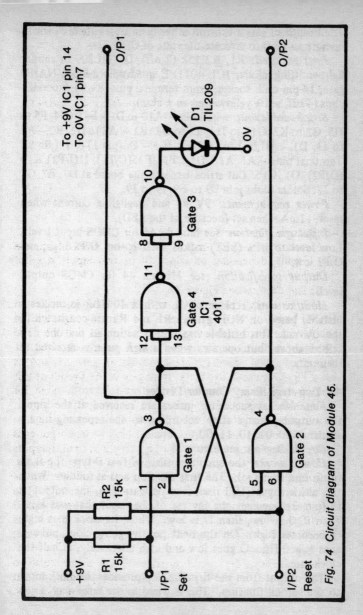

Fig. 74 Circuit diagram of Module 45.

111

The output of gate 1 is inverted twice by Gates 4 and 3, which operate an LED to indicate the state of O/P1.

Parts required: R1, R2 15k (2 off), D1 TIL209 or similar light-emitting diode, IC1 4011BE quadruple 2-input NAND gate, 14-pin d.i.l. socket, 1mm terminal pins (8 off), crocodile clips (4 off, red + yellow + green + blue).

Stripboard layout: wire links – A10 to D10, E4 to G4, F5 to H5, G2 to K2, G11 to I11, J5 to O5. R1 – A2 to D2. R2 – A3 to I3. D1 – H12(a) to O12(k). IC1 – D6(pin 1) to J9(pin 8). Terminal pins – A1, A15, D1(I/P1), F15(O/P1), I1(I/P2), K15 (O/P2), O1, O15. Cut strips beneath the board at D7, E7, G7 to J7. Solder blobs join E9 to F9, I9 to J9.

Power requirements: 9V dc and negligible current when reset, 11mA when set (because of the LED).

Input specification: see Module 44 for CMOS input levels. Low level to I/P1 (SET) makes LED go on, O/P1 high, and O/P2 low.

Output specification: see Module 44 for CMOS output levels.

Modifications: replacing IC1 with a 4001BE ic, makes a bistable based on NOR gates. R1 and R2 are connected to the 0V rail. This bistable has similar action to the one described above, but operates when a *high* pulse is received at its inputs.

46 Two-stage Binary Counter/Divider

Function: as successive pulses are received at the input, the outputs change state according to the repeating binary sequence 00, 01, 10, 11, 00, . . . etc.

Circuit diagram: see Figure 75.

How it works: the circuit consists of two D-type flip-flops (both in a single ic). The first flip-flop acts as follows. When the clock input (I/P) rises from low to high, the output at $\overline{Q}$ (pin 2) becomes the inverse of the input that was at D. Thus if $\overline{Q}$ is low, then D is low. When the clock goes high, $\overline{Q}$ becomes high. On the next positive-going clock pulse $\overline{Q}$ goes low. Thus $\overline{Q}$ goes low and high alternately, at half the clock rate.

The output from the first flip-flop provides the clock input to the second flip-flop. This is wired in the same way, so its

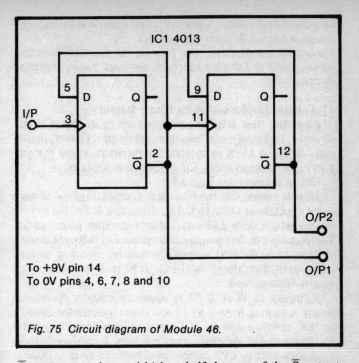

IC1 4013

5 D Q

9 D Q

I/P 3

11

2 Q̄

12 Q̄

O/P2

O/P1

To +9V pin 14
To 0V pins 4, 6, 7, 8 and 10

Fig. 75 Circuit diagram of Module 46.

Q̄ output goes low and high at half the rate of the Q̄ output of the first flip-flop, i.e. at one-quarter the rate of I/P. Thus, this module acts as a frequency divider. Since the outputs change in the sequence listed earlier, it can also be used as a binary counter.

Parts required: IC1 4013BE CMOS dual D-type flip-flop, 14-pin d.i.l. socket, 1mm terminal pins (7 off), crocodile clips (3 off, red + yellow + blue).

Stripboard layout: wire links — A10 to E10, D12 to G12, G11 to J11, I10 to K10, F4 to I4, F5 to H10, G2 to I2, H3 to K3, K5 to O5. IC1 — E6(pin 1) to K9(pin 8). Terminal pins — A1, A15, D15(O/P2), H15(O/P1), I1, O1, O15. Cut strips beneath the board at E7 to J7 (NOT at K7), I3. Solder blob jobs J6 to K6.

Power requirements: 9V dc and negligible current.

Input specification: see Module 44 for CMOS input levels.

113

Module changes state when I/P rises from low to high (no change when it falls from high to low).

Output specification: see Module 44 for CMOS output levels. O/P1 and O/P2 go through a 4-stage binary sequence, described above.

47 Counter/Divider with 4-Bit Binary Output

Function: this counter can count up or down, in binary (0 to 15, repeating) or in binary coded decimal (0 to 9, repeating). It has 4 LEDs to indicate its output state and the outputs of the ic are available for driving other modules.

Circuit diagram: see Figure 76.

How it works: this is a four-stage counter, the four outputs being available at O/P1 to O/P4. The count is also fed to four buffers which drive LEDs to indicate the state of the count. The counter can be operated in a number of different modes:

1) up or down: if S1 is open, the counter counts up on each rising input from the clock (I/P1). If S1 is closed, the counter counts down instead.

2) binary or BCD: if S2 is open, the counter operates in binary, counting from 0 to 15 and then repeating (or from 15 to 0 if counting down). If S2 is closed the counter operates in binary coded decimal, counting from 0 to 9 or 9 to 0.

A high level to I/P2 causes the counter to reset to 0000 at any state of the clock. I/P2 must be restored to a low level to allow counting to proceed.

Output O/P5 is used when cascading two modules to give an 8-bit binary or 2-digit BCD count. This output goes low on count 9 (BCD) or count 15 (binary). See *Modifications* below for details on how to use this output.

The counter is *synchronous* so that all outputs that are due to change state do so simultaneously. This prevents spurious transition counts from appearing at the outputs.

Parts required: R1–R3 15k (3 off), C1 100n polyester, IC1 4029BE presettable binary/BCD up/down counter, IC2 4050BE hex non-inverting buffer, D1–D4 TIL209 or similar LEDs (4 off), S1/S2 dual SPST d.i.l. switch, 16-pin d.i.l. sockets (2 off), stripboard 28 holes by 16 strips, 1mm terminal pins (11 off), crocodile clips (4 off, red + yellow + green + blue).

114

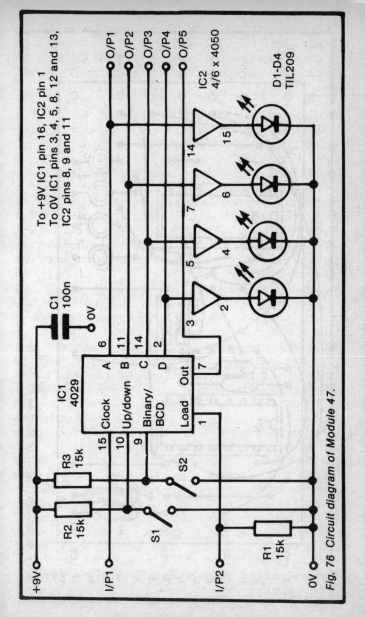

Fig. 76 Circuit diagram of Module 47.

115

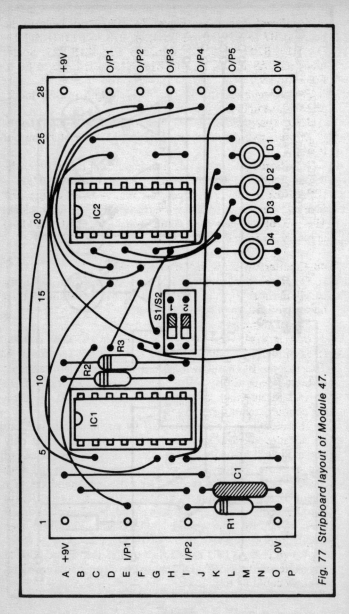

Fig. 77 Stripboard layout of Module 47.

116

Stripboard layout: see Figure 77. Cut strips beneath the board at B7 to D7, G7 to I7, E3, I4, B13 to F13, G14, H13, I13, H17, B20 to H20, F26, H26, J26, L26, K21, L23. Solder blobs join A9 to B9, A19 to B19, H15 to I15, D6 to E6 to F6, E9 to F9.

Power requirements: 9V dc. Up to 40mA in BCD mode; up to 50mA in binary mode.

Input specification: see Module 44 for CMOS input levels.

Output specification: see Module 44 for CMOS output levels.

Modifications: to cascade two modules of this type, the second module must be modified to give access to pin 5 (ENABLE) of IC1. Connect this pin to O/P5 of the first module. Connect I/P1 of *both* modules to the same clock. The pair of modules then count from 0 to 127 (11111111) in binary, or from 0 to 99 in BCD.

48 Counter/Divider with Numeric Display

Function: this counter can count up or down, in binary coded decimal (0 to 9 repeating). It has a 7-segment LED numeric display to indicate the count.

Circuit diagram: see Figure 78.

How it works: this module is based on the same counter ic as Module 47. Its output is fed to a 4511 decoder ic. This accepts BCD and switches on the appropriate segments of the numeric display. If S1 is open, the counter counts up on each rising input from the clock (I/P1). If S1 is closed, the counter counts down instead.

The module is designed so that two or more modules can be cascaded to make a display of 2 or more digits. If only one module is being used, or for the first module of a chain of two or more, switch S2 is set to connect pin 5 of IC1 with the 0V rail. For the second and subsequent modules of a chain, S2 is set to connect pin 5 with I/P3. Connect I/P3 to the O/P terminal of the preceding module. The clock input goes to I/P1 of all modules in the chain. The chain then counts from 00 to 99, or from 000 to 999, etc.

A high level to I/P2 causes the counter to reset to 0000 at any state of the clock. I/P2 must be restored to a low level to allow counting to proceed.

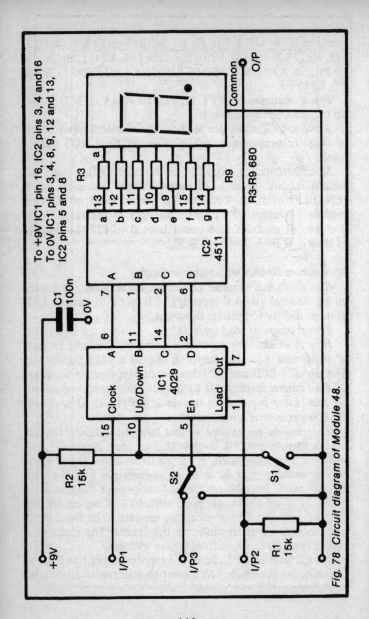

To +9V IC1 pin 16, IC2 pins 3, 4 and 16,
To 0V IC1 pins 3, 4, 8, 9, 12 and 13,
IC2 pins 5 and 8

Fig. 78 Circuit diagram of Module 48.

118

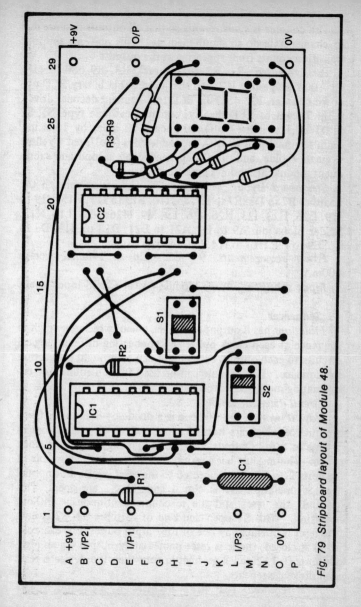

Fig. 79 Stripboard layout of Module 48.

119

The counter is *synchronous* so that all outputs that are due to change state do so simultaneously. This prevents spurious transition counts from appearing at the outputs.

Parts required: R1–R2 15k (2 off), R3–R9 680 (7 off), C1 100n polyester, IC1 4029BE presettable binary/BCD up/down counter, IC2 4511BE BCD to 7-segment decoder driver, 0.3in 7-segment LED display, common cathode type, S1, S2 SPDT d.i.l. switch (2 off), stripboard 29 holes by 16 strips, 1mm terminal pins (8 off), crocodile clips (4 off, red + yellow + green + blue, additional clip needed on second and subsequent module, if modules are cascaded).

Stripboard layout: see Figure 79. Cut strips beneath the board at B7 to D7, F7 to H7, J5, I10, B13 to I13, H15, B19 to I19, E26, H23, I23, H26, I26, L9, M9, M26, N26, L13, M13. Solder blobs join A9 to B9, A21 to B21, D18 to E18, D6 to E6, E9 to F9, H14 to I14, L10 to M10.

Power requirements: 9V dc. Up to 140mA, average 100mA.

Input specification: see Module 44 for CMOS input levels.

49 Sequencer

Function: has 8 output terminals, one of which goes high in sequence at each clock pulse. By connecting different logical circuits to each output, each circuit can be brought into action in sequence. This module can be used for controlling and co-ordinating multi-stage processing.

Circuit diagram: see Figure 80.

How it works: the 4022 ic is a divide-by-8 counter, the 8 outputs of which are normally low, but which go high one at a time in turn. Outputs change on the rising edge of the clock pulse. The module has a series of switches which allow one of outputs 2 to 7 to be connected to the reset input. For normal 8-stage operation, S1 is closed and S2–S7 are open. This grounds the reset and the ic counts continuously without resetting. With S1 open and *one* of switches S2–S7 closed, the reset is operated by one of the output pulses. For example, if S4 is closed, the ic is reset immediately output 4 goes high. Outputs 0, 1, 2 and 3 go high in turn then the device is reset and the cycle repeats.

Parts required: IC1 4022 BE divide-by-8 counter, S1–S7

120

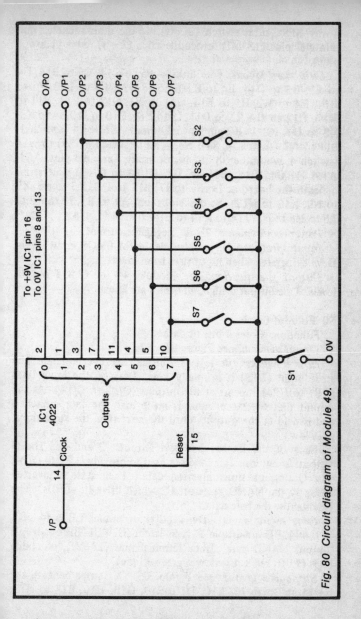

Fig. 80 Circuit diagram of Module 49.

121

4-way SPST d.i.l. switch (2 off), 16-pin d.i.l. socket, 1mm terminal pins (13 off), crocodile clips (3 off, red + yellow + blue).

Stripboard layout: wire links — B5 to C14, C5 to B14, D4 to L2, D5 to D14, E4 to K10, E5 to G14, F4 to L10, F5 to H14, H4 to M2, H5 to E14, G11 to N2, G12 to F14, H11 to M10, H12 to I14, I2 to D11, I5 to E11, C10 to J10, I4 to K3, K2 to O2. IC1 — B6(pin 1) to I9(pin 9). S1 — K4 (switch 1, S1) to N7 (switch 4, S4). S2 — K11 (switch 1, S5) to N14 (switch 4, would be S8 but is not used). Terminal pins — A1, A15, I1, O1, O15, B15 to I15 (O/P0 to O/P7). Cut strips beneath the board at I3, B7 to I7, B13 to I13, K5 to N5, K9 to N9, K12 to N12. Solder blobs join A9 to B9, J8 to K8 to L8 to M8 to N8, J14 to K14 to L14 to M14 to N14.

Power requirements: 9V dc, negligible current.

Input specification: see Module 44 for CMOS input levels. Device operates when input rises from low to high.

Output specification: see Module 44 for CMOS output levels. One output is high, all others are low.

50 Four-bit Latch

Function: stores 4 bits of data.

Circuit diagram: see Figure 81.

How it works: the ic is a 4-bit clocked D-type latch. The store input (I/P5) is normally low. Data on the input lines (I/P1 to I/P4) appears at the outputs (O/P1 to O/P4). At the instant that the store input is made high the data is latched and is held at the outputs until the next time the store input goes low.

Each of the latches has two outputs, Q and $\bar{Q}$. The Q outputs show true data, and are used to provide O/P1 to O/P4. The $\bar{Q}$ outputs show inverted data. Their state is inverted again by the NAND gates of IC2 which drive the LEDs. The LEDs show the true data.

Parts required: D1–D4 TIL209 or similar LEDs (4 off), IC1 4042BE quadruple D-type latch, IC2 4011BE quadruple 2-input NAND gate, 1mm terminal pins (13 off), crocodile clips (7 off, red + 4 yellow + green + blue).

Stripboard layout: see Figure 82. Cut strips beneath the board at B6 to I6, B10, D10, E10, G10, H10, B13 to H13,

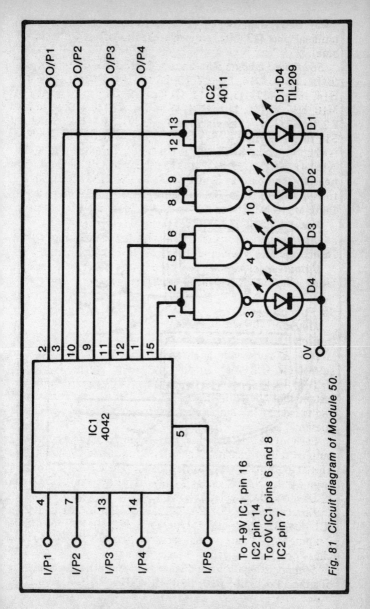

Fig. 81 Circuit diagram of Module 50.

To +9V IC1 pin 16
IC2 pin 14
To 0V IC1 pins 6 and 8
IC2 pin 7

123

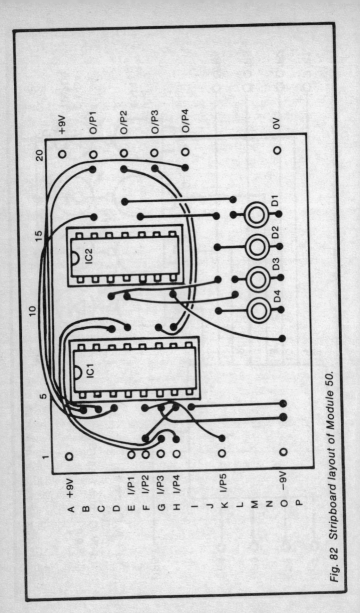

Fig. 82 Stripboard layout of Module 50.

124

C18, E18, G18, I18, F3, G3, H3, K3, K13, L14. Solder blobs join A8 to B8, B12 to C12, A15 to B15, C15 to D15, F12 to G12, G15 to H15 to I15.

Power requirements: 9V dc, negligible current.

Input specification: see Module 44 for CMOS input levels. All inputs must be connected either to the output from another module, the +9V rail or the 0V rail.

Output specification: see Module 44 for CMOS output levels. The module can be used simply as a data indicator with no connections made to its outputs.

Modifications: if pin 6 of IC1 is connected to +9V instead of 0V, the device latches as I/P5 goes low.

51 Pulse Generator

Function: this is a monostable that produces a pulse when it is triggered. The length of the pulse is not accurately constant (for this use Module 43), but the circuit is simple and inexpensive and is useful for a variety of purposes.

Circuit diagram: see Figure 83.

How it works: normally the input is high. The output of gate 1 is low, so gate 2 receives a low input from this gate and a high input from C1, which is charged. Consequently, its output (O/P1) is high (see the NAND truth table, Module 44). Gate 3 inverts this to give a low output at O/P2. When I/P goes low, the output of gate 1 immediately changes to high. Now gate 2 is receiving two high inputs, for C1 has not had time to discharge. The output of gate 2 goes low, and the output of gate 3 goes high. Gradually the charge on C1 leaks away through R1 and the input level to gate 2 falls. When it has fallen to a low level, gate 2 has one high and one low input, so its output changes to high again. Thus gate 2 has produced a short low pulse. The input level may then rise again but this does not affect gate 2; when the output of gate 1 changes to low, gate 2 receives two low inputs and its output stays high; when C1 is re-charged, gate 2 has one low and one high input and its output is high, as at the beginning.

Parts required: R1 10k, C1 100n polyester layer, IC1 4011 quadruple 2-input NAND gate, 14-pin d.i.l. socket, 1mm terminal pins (7 off), crocodile clips (3 off, red + yellow + blue).

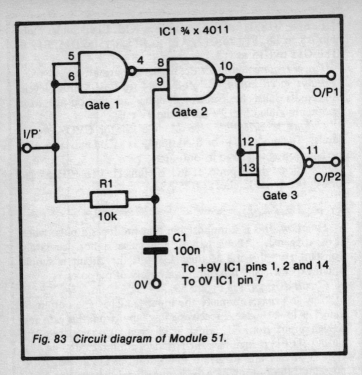

Fig. 83 Circuit diagram of Module 51.

Stripboard layout: wire links — A10 to D10, F11 to H11, I11 to L11, G5 to J10, J4 to O4. R1 — I3 to L3. C1 — L7 to O7. IC1 — D6 (pin 1) to J9 (pin 8). Terminal pins — A1, A15, F15(O/P2), H15(O/P1), I1, O1, O15. Cut strips beneath the board at E7 to J7, F13. Solder blobs join D6 to E6, H6 to I6, E9 to F9, F15 to G15.

Power requirements: 9V dc, negligble current.

Input specification: see Module 44 for CMOS input levels. Triggered when the input falls from high to low.

Output specification: see Module 44 for CMOS output levels. O/P1 is normally high, giving a low pulse when triggered. O/P2 is the inverse of this. Pulse length is approximately 1.5ms.

Modifications: use a 4001BE instead to give pulses on a rising input level; O/P1 gives a low pulse, O/P2 gives a high pulse.

126

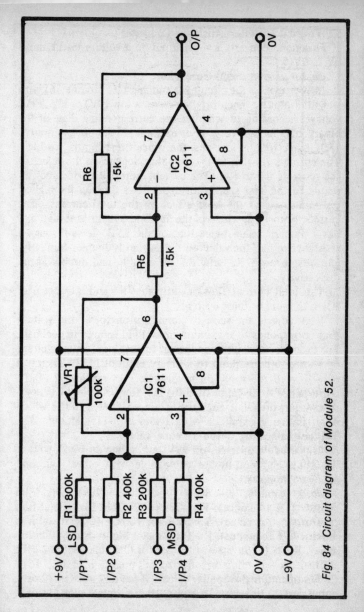

Fig. 84 Circuit diagram of Module 52.

127

52 Four-bit Digital-to-Analogue Converter

Function: converts a 4-bit input to a voltage in the range 0V to 9V.

Circuit diagram: see Figure 84.

How it works: the circuit is a summer (see Module 36) with weighted inputs. Each input receives a low (0V) or high (9V) voltage, according to whether the corresponding digit of the binary number is 0 or 1. For example, if the binary input is 1101 then I/P2 is low and the other three inputs are high. The currents flowing to the amplifier depend on the values of the resistors R1 to R4. The current from I/P1, which corresponds to the least significant digit, flows through the highest resistance, so has the least effect on the total current. The current from I/P2, which in the next most significant digit and has a numeric value twice that of the LSD, flows through a resistance of half the value, so the current is double. Similarly, currents through R3 and R4 are double and double again, respectively.

The total current flowing through VR1 and into pin 6 of IC1 is the sum of these currents.

VR1 adjusts the scale of amplification to set the voltage that corresponds to maximum input (1111, or 15 in decimal). For example, it may be convenient to have a maximum voltage of -1.5V to correspond to a binary input of 1111. Then it is easy to read the value on a voltmeter. A reading of -0.6V corresponds to an input of 6 (0110), for example. The negative output of IC1 is not easy to use, so it is fed to IC2 which is an inverting amplifier with a gain of 1 (see Module 32). This gives a positive output of equal value.

This module operates on ±9V rather than on ±4.5V so that its inputs and output are compatible with other logic and analogue modules.

Parts required: R1 800k (or 330k + 470k) metal film resistor (1% tolerance), R2 400k (or 390k + 10k) metal film resistor (1% tolerance), R3 200k (or 100k + 100k) metal film resistor (1% tolerance), R4 100k metal film resistor (1% tolerance), R5, R6 15k metal film resistor (1% tolerance) (2 off), VR1 100k sub-miniature horizontal preset, IC1, IC2 7611 CMOS operational amplifier (2 off), 8-pin d.i.l. sockets (2 off), stripboard 22 holes by 16 strips, 1mm terminal pins (11 off),

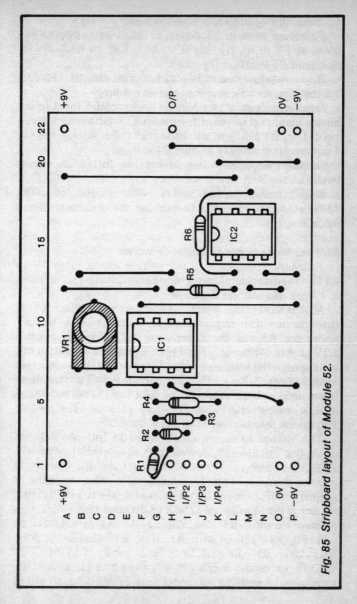

Fig. 85 Stripboard layout of Module 52.

129

crocodile clips (7 off, red + 4 yellow + blue + black).

Stripboard layout: see Figure 85. Cut strips beneath the board at F8 to I8, H5, I5, H20, K13, K15 to N15. Solder blob joins C7 to D7.

Power requirements: ±9V dc, negligible current. Module 2 is the most suitable source of the −9V supply.

Input specification: see Module 44 for CMOS input levels. Inputs could also be taken from a set of 4 switches, connecting the inputs either to 0V or to +9V. For testing, use the 4 outputs from a binary counter (Module 47).

Output specification: see Module 44 for CMOS output levels.

Modifications: further inputs, with resistors of 160k, 320k, etc., can be added to increase the resolution of the module.

53 Four-bit Analogue-to-Digital Converter

Function: converts an input voltage in the range 0V to 0.15V (approximately) to a 4-bit binary output.

Circuit diagram: see Figure 86.

How it works: this module is based on a specialised A-to-D converter ic. This requires a supply voltage of 4.5V to 5.5V so we use R1 and the Zener diode D1 to provide a stable 5.1V supply for the ic. The ZN427E has an 8-bit output but we use only the least significant four bits in this module (see *Modifications*, below). The four outputs switch on transistors when high, causing the LEDs to light and the corresponding module outputs (O/P1 to O/P4) to go low. The module outputs are thus the inverse of the ic outputs.

The voltage to be converted is fed to I/P1. An external clock (e.g. Module 18, operating at about 1kHz) connected at I/P3 is required to drive the converter circuits. Conversion begins when S1 is briefly pressed, or a logic low pulse is applied to I/P2. A fraction of a second (about 130ms) later, the lamps light to show the result of the conversion.

Parts required: R1 150, R2 3k3, R3 390, R4–R7 2k2 (4 off), R8–R11 180 (4 off), R12 82k, R13 15k, C1 1μ polyester layer, D1 BZY88C5V1 Zener diode, 5.1V, D2–D5 TIL209 or similar LEDs (4 off), 18-pin d.i.l. socket, S1 push-to-make push-button, stripboard 27 holes by 16 strips,

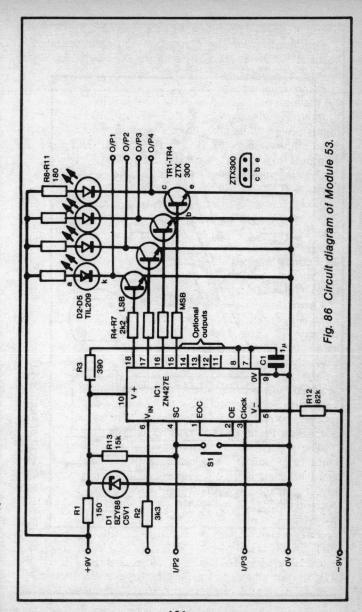

Fig. 86 Circuit diagram of Module 53.

131

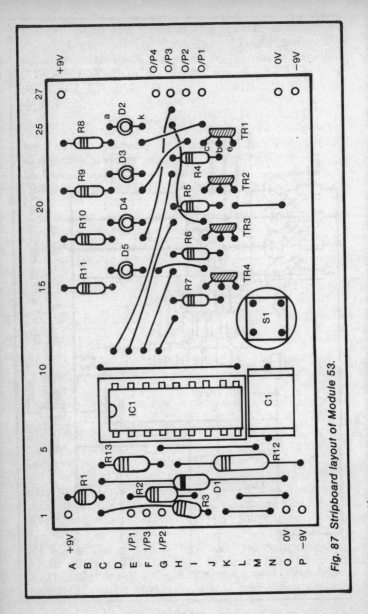

Fig. 87 Stripboard layout of Module 53.

132

1mm terminal pins (13 off), crocodile clips (6 off, red + 3 yellow + blue + black).

Stripboard layout: see Figure 87. Cut strips beneath the board at D7 to L7, D12 to L12, D17, D20, D23, E3, F17, F20, F23, H15, H18, H21, H24, J17, J20, J23, K16, K19, K22, and N7. Solder blobs join D6 to E6, J6 to K6, F16 to G16, I22 to J22, and N10 to O10.

Power requirements: ±9V dc, about 30mA.

Input specification: voltage in the range 0 to 0.15V. Use a potential divider (Module 9) if a higher source of voltage is to be converted. A short low pulse to I/P2, such as obtained from a pulse generator (Module 51, O/P1) will start conversion.

Output specification: outputs are compatible with CMOS logic, but must be inverted if it is important for them to be in true binary. Module 44 could be used with the gate inputs connected in pairs to make the NAND gates into INVERT gates.

Modifications: the other 4 outputs of the ic may be used, and the maximum input voltage is then increased to 2.5V.

D – OUTPUT MODULES

54 Indicators

Function: a set of four LEDs to indicate the output state of logical circuits.

Circuit diagram: the module consists of 4 inverters and LEDs connected as shown in Figure 88.

How it works: each NAND gate has its inputs wired together, so that it acts as an inverter (see truth table, Module 44). When an I/P is high, the output of the gate goes low. This sinks current through the LED, causing it to light.

Parts required: D1–D4 TIL209 or similar LEDs (4 off), IC1 4011BE quadruple 2-input NAND gate, 14-pin d.i.l. socket, 1mm terminal pins (8 off), crocodile clips (6 off, red + 4 yellow + blue).

Stripboard layout: wire links – A13 to G13, D6 to I6, D14 to K14, E4 to H4, E8 to J8, E12 to J13, G3 to L3, I4 to L13, K4 to H13, M8 to O8. D1 – A5(a) to D5(k). D2 – A7(a) to E7(k). D3 – A9(a) to D9(k). D4 – A11(a) to

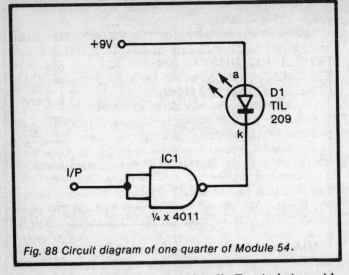

Fig. 88 Circuit diagram of one quarter of Module 54.

E11(k). IC1 — G9(pin 1) to M12(pin 8). Terminal pins — A1, A15, E1(I/P1), G1(I/P2), I1(I/P3), K1(I/P4), O1, O15. Cut strips beneath the board at D7, E5, E9, G5, I5, K5, G10 to M10. Solder blobs join G9 to H9, K9 to L9, H12 to I12, L12 to M12.

Power requirements: 9V dc. 10mA for each LED in use.

Input specification: see Module 44 for CMOS input levels.

Modifications: LEDs of different colours may be used.

55 Transistor Switch and Indicator (type 1)

Function: to supply power to a load, such as a lamp, buzzer, motor, or small relay, with an LED to indicate its state.

Circuit diagram: see Figure 89.

How it works: when the input voltage rises, base current flows to TR1, turning it on. Collector current flows through the load, the transistor and R2. The flow of current through R2 generates a small potential difference across it. Current then flows to the base of TR2, turning it on, and through the LED D2, making it light. The other diode D1 is to protect the circuit against damage should the load be an inductive one. If the current through such a load (an electric bell, motor or

134

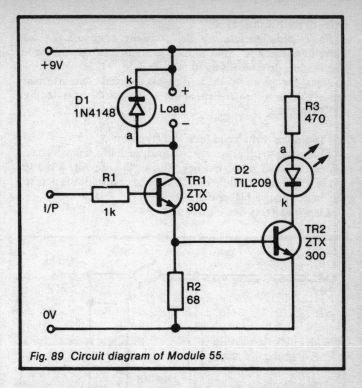

Fig. 89 Circuit diagram of Module 55.

relay) is suddenly turned off a *back e.m.f.* of several tens of volts, possibly greater, is generated as the magnetic field in its coils collapses. This causes a large reverse current to flow through TR1, and is likely to destroy it. If the diode is present, the current flows safely through this instead.

Parts required: R1 1k, R2 68, R3 470, D1 1N4148 silicon signal diode, D2 TIL209 or similar light emitting diode, TR1, TR2 ZTX300 npn transistor (2 off), 1mm terminal pins (6 off), crocodile clips (3 off, red + yellow + blue).

Stripboard layout: wire link – K11 to O11. R1 – I2 to I5. R2 – J5 to O5. R3 – A6 to D6. D1 – A13(k, band) to H13(a). D2 – D9(a) to I9(k, flat). TR1 – H7(c), I7(b) and J7(e). TR2 – I10(c), J10(b) and K10(e). Terminal pins – A1, A15 (load positive), H15 (load negative), I1, O1, O15. Cut strips

135

beneath the board at I3, I8.

Power requirements: 9V dc. Current when off is zero. Current when on is 15mA plus the current drawn by the load. The module drives loads up to 500mA.

Input specification: the load begins to receive current when input voltage is greater than about 1.5V. Can be operated by CMOS outputs.

56 Transistor Switch and Indicator (type 2)

Function: to supply power to a load, such as a lamp, buzzer, motor, or small relay, but operating in the opposite sense to Module 55. The module can be used to control loads operating on dc voltages higher than 9V.

Circuit diagram: see Figure 90.

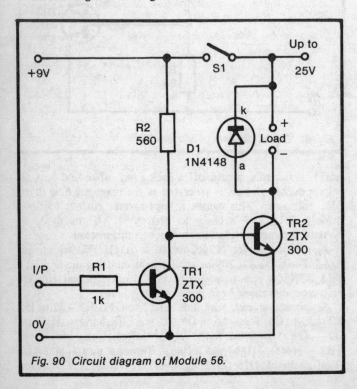

Fig. 90 Circuit diagram of Module 56.

136

How it works: when input voltage is zero or close to zero, TR1 is off, the voltage at its collector is high, and base current is flowing to TR2, which is on. Current is passed through the load. When the input voltage rises, base current flows to TR1, turning it on. This reduces the voltage at its collector, reducing the base current flowing to TR2 and turning it off. No current flows through the load. Diode D1 is to protect the circuit against damage, as explained for Module 55.

The module is operated in either of two modes:

1) S1 closed: for loads operating on 9V dc and powered by the same supply that powers the module;

2) S1 open: for loads powered by an external dc supply, which may be up to 25V.

Parts required: R1 1k, R2 560, D1 1N4148 silicon signal diode, TR1, TR2, ZTX300 npn transistor (2 off), S1 SPDT d.i.l. switch, 1mm terminal pins (6 off), crocodile clips (3 off, red + yellow + blue).

Stripboard layout: wire link − K8 to O8. R1 − I3 to J3. R2 − A8 to I8. D1 − A14(k, band) to H14(a). TR1 − I6(c), J6(b) and K6(e). TR2 − H10(c), I10(b) and K10(e). S1 − A10/B10 and A13/B13. Terminal pins − A1, A15 (load positive, external power supply if used). H16 (load negative) I1, O1, O15. Cut strips beneath the board at A11, I5.

Power requirements: 9V dc. Current is 17mA plus load (up to 500mA).

Input specification: the load receives no current when input voltage is greater than about 1.5V. The input can be operated by a CMOS output.

57 Power Transistor Switch

Function: for switching current to heavy loads such as heavy-duty relays, solenoids, motors (model electric trains), and high-power lamps. The module may be used with devices that require up to 60V dc supply.

Circuit diagram: see Figure 91.

How it works: TR1 is a VMOS n-channel field effect power transistor, switched on by a positive voltage at its gate. D1 protects the transistor from damage when powering inductive loads (see Module 55).

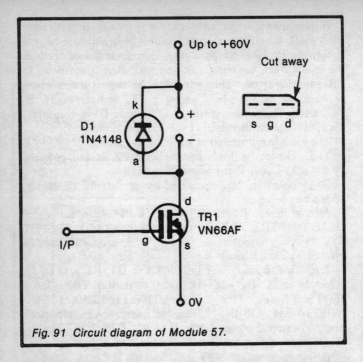

Fig. 91 Circuit diagram of Module 57.

Parts required: D1 1N4148 silicon signal diode, TR1 VN66AF VMOS field effect power transistor, 1mm terminal pins (6 off), crocodile clips (3 off, red + yellow + blue).

Stripboard layout: wire link — J6 to O6. D1 — A11(k, band) to H11(a). TR1 — H8(d), I8(g), J8(s). Terminal pins — A1, A15 (load positive), H15 (load negative), I1, O1, O15.

Power requirements: 9V dc or up to 60V dc from an external power supply. The module must not be connected to the 9V system positive supply if it is connected to an external power supply that is not 9V. Requires no current when off. Requires load current when on (maximum 1.8A).

Input specification: switches on when voltage exceeds the gate threshold, which is in the range 0.8V to 2V. The gate requires no current, so input impedance is very high. It can be operated by a CMOS output.

138

58 Relay Driver

Function: switches a relay that has SPDT contacts.
Circuit diagram: see Figure 92.

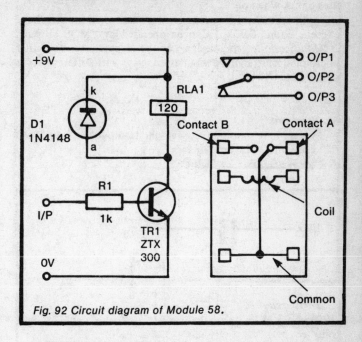

Fig. 92 Circuit diagram of Module 58.

How it works: when a positive voltage is applied to I/P the transistor is switched on. Current flows through the relay coil and the relay operates. Contact between O/P1 and O/P2 is broken; contact betwen O/P2 and O/P3 is made. The diode is to protect the transistor from damage (see Module 55).

Parts required: R1 1k, D1 1N4148, TR1 ZTX300 npn transistor, RLA1 micro-miniature relay, with SPDT contacts, nominal operating voltage 6V dc. 1mm terminal pins (8 off), crocodile clips (3 off, red + yellow + blue).

Stripboard layout: wire links — A13 to F13, E8 to K8, H6 to O6. R1 — G3 to I3. D1 — A7(k, band) to F7(a). TR1 — F5(c), G5(b), H5(e). RLA1 — E9(contact B) to H11(common).

Terminal pins — A1, A15, E15(O/P3), H15(O/P2), K15(O/P1), I1, O1, O15. Cut strips beneath the board at E10, F10.

Power requirements: 9V dc. Uses no current when off, uses 65mA when on.

Input specification: turns on the relay when input voltage exceeds about 0.75V. Can be operated by CMOS outputs.

Modifications: the design can be adapted to use other micro-miniature and ultra-miniature relays with different types of contact.

59 Earphone

Function: a simple crystal earphone module for use with radio sets and audio amplifiers.

Circuit diagram: see Figure 93.

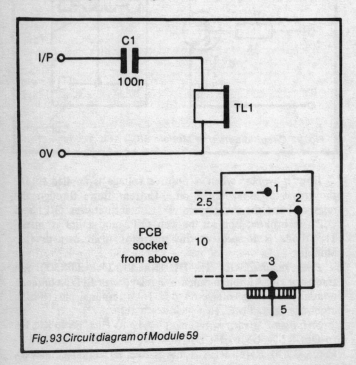

Fig. 93 Circuit diagram of Module 59

140

How it works: the signal passes across the coupling capacitor and activates the piezo-electric element of the earphone.

Parts required: C1 100n polyester layer, TL1 crystal earphone, high-impedance type as used with transistor radio sets, 3.5mm mono jack socket, pcb mounting, 1mm terminal pins (3 off), crocodile clips (2 off, yellow + blue).

Stripboard layout: wire link – H6 to O6. C1 – F4 to I4. Socket – H8(1), F9(2), and H13(3). Terminal pins – I1, O1, O15.

Power requirements: none.

Input specification: accepts inputs from audio amplifiers.

Modifications: the socket is intended for the 3.5mm mono jack plug usually supplied on a transistor-set ear-plug. Alternatively the plug can be cut off and soldered directly to two terminal pins at F15 and H15. If this is done, the socket is not required.

60 Earphone with Amplifier

Function: a crystal earphone with an amplifier.

Circuit diagram: see Figure 94.

How it works: the transistor is biassed by current flowing through R2 and R1. The audio signal is passed across C1 and adds to or subtracts from that current. The variations in the base current causes corresponding variations in the collector current. As the current through R2 varies, the voltage across it varies too and this produces an audio signal from the earphone.

Parts required: R1 100k, R2 10k, R3 270, C1 100n polyester layer, TR1 ZTX300 npn transistor, TL1 crystal earphone, high-impedance type as used with transistor radio sets, 3.5mm mono jack socket, pcb mounting, 1mm terminal pins (5 off), crocodile clips (3 off, red + yellow + blue).

Stripboard layout: wire link – C6 to K8. R1 – K7 to L7. R2 – A5 to K5. R3 – M11 to O11. C1 – I3 to L3. TR1 – K9(c), L9(b), M9(e). Socket (see Fig.93) – C8(1), A9(2), C13(3). Terminal pins – A1, A15, I1, O1, O15.

Power requirements: 9V dc. Current 10mA.

Input specification: accepts inputs from audio amplifiers.

Modifications: the socket is intended for the 3.5mm mono jack plug usually supplied on a transistor-set ear-plug. Alter-

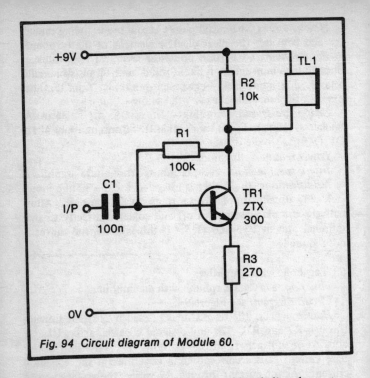

Fig. 94 *Circuit diagram of Module 60.*

tively the plug can be cut off and soldered directly to two terminal pins at A9 and C9. The socket is not required.

61 Sounder

Function: a simple audio-output module, particularly suitable for use as a buzzer, or for audible warning applications.

Circuit diagram: the circuit is the same as in Figure 93, except that a crystal sounder replaces the earphone.

How it works: the signal passes across the coupling capacitor and activates the piezo-electric element of the sounder.

Parts required: C1 100n polyester layer, XTAL1 piezo-electric sounder, 1mm terminal pins (5 off), crocodile clips (2 off, yellow + blue).

142

Stripboard layout: drill holes to mount the sounder, centring it at H11. Attach the sounder securely to the board, as this increases the volume of sound obtained. Wire link – from the pins at F5 and O5 to the two terminals of the sounder. C1 – F4 to I4. Terminal pins – I1, F5, O1, O5, O15.

Power requirements: none.

Input specification: accepts inputs from square-wave generators, such as Modules 18 and 40. Signals of about 4kHz usually produce the loudest output.

62 Loudspeaker

Function: a simple loudspeaker module for use with radio sets and audio amplifiers.

Circuit diagram: see Figure 95.

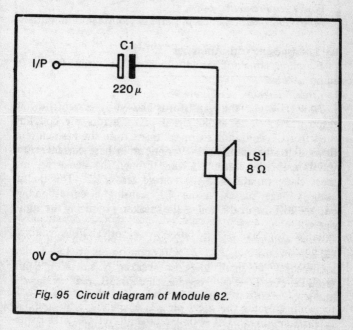

Fig. 95 Circuit diagram of Module 62.

How it works: the signal passes across the coupling capacitor and activates the coil of the loudspeaker.

143

Parts required: C1 220μ electrolytic, LS1 8-ohm loudspeaker (a small low-cost speaker is suitable), 1mm terminal pins (5 off), crocodile clips (2 off, yellow + blue).

Stripboard layout: the simplest construction is to mount the speaker on the board, using bolts and clips or epoxy-resin adhesive. Better reproduction is obtained if the speaker is mounted in an enclosure, which could be a plastic instrument case. A small cased speaker, such as is used in a car radio system would be very suitable. If the speaker is cased, solder the negative terminal of C1 to a terminal of the speaker. Solder one lead (blue) to the other speaker terminal, and another lead (yellow) to the positive terminal of C1.

If the speaker is mounted on stripboard, the standard layout is: C1 – F4(–) to I4(+). Terminal pins – I1, F6 (speaker), O1, O6 (speaker), O15.

Power requirements: none.

Input specification: accepts inputs from audio amplifiers.

63 Loudspeaker with Amplifier

Function: an amplifier with loudspeaker output for use in audio systems.

Circuit diagram: see Figure 96.

How it works: the transistor is biassed by current flowing through R1. The audio signal passes across the coupling capacitor C1 and adds to or subtracts from the base current flowing to the transistor. Variations in base current cause variations in the current flowing through the transistor, and these cause variations in the voltage across R2. This fluctuating voltage passes across C2, causing a corresponding current to flow in the coil of the speaker, producing the audio output.

Parts required: R1 56k, R2 330, C1 100n polyester layer, C2 22μ electrolytic, TR1 ZTX300 npn transistor, LS1 8-ohm loudspeaker (a small low-cost speaker is suitable), 1mm terminal pins (7 off), crocodile clips (3 off, red + yellow + blue).

Stripboard layout: the loudspeaker is best mounted in an enclosure (see Module 62), with the stripboard mounted inside. Wire link – A11 to E11. R1 – A5 to F5. R2 – G10 to O10. C1 – F3 to I3. C2 – G13(+) to M13. TR1 – E8(c), F8(b),

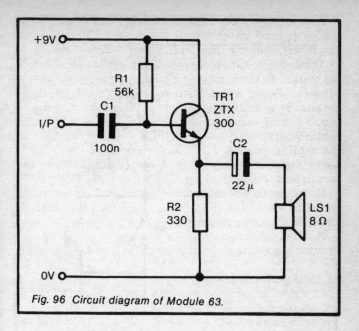

Fig. 96 Circuit diagram of Module 63.

G8(e). Terminal pins – A1, A15, I1, M15 (loudspeaker), O1, O15 (loudspeaker).

Power requirements: 9V dc. 10mA.

Input specification: audio input from amplifiers.

64 Infra-red Transmitter

Function: a source of infra-red radiation, either for intruder-detection beams or for remote control.

Circuit diagram: see Figure 97.

How it works: the infra-red LED, D1, emits radiation when S1 is closed or S2 is pressed. S1 is for continuous use when the module is being used to produce a beam. S2 is for intermittent use in remote control systems.

Parts required: R1 47, 3W, D1 TIL78 large infra-red diode, S1 SPDT d.i.l. switch, S2 push-to-make push-button, 1mm terminal pins (4 off), crocodile clips (2 off, red + blue).

Stripboard layout: wire links – K3 to O3, L9 to O9. R1 – A3 to E3.   D1 – E9(a), J9(k, flat).   S1 – J4/K4, J7/K7

145

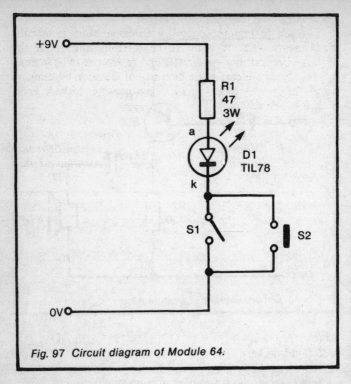

Fig. 97 Circuit diagram of Module 64.

(common, see Fig.57). S2 – J10/J12, L10/L12 (see Fig.23). Terminal pins – A1, A15, O1, O15. Cut strip beneath the board at K5.

Power requirements: 9V dc. 150mA.

Modifications: if the module is intended only for intermittent flashes, R1 can be replaced by a 1W resistor of the same resistance. If the module is to be used to produce a beam (e.g. for intruder detection), it is improved by mounting the board in an enclosure, such as a plastic case. An aperture is cut in the case to allow IR to escape in the required direction. Bend the leads of the diode to point the apex of the diode in the direction the beam is to go. It is further improved if a converging lens is mounted in the aperture to focus the radiation into a parallel-sided beam. The diode

146

should be at the focal point of the lens.

For use in remote control, a focussed beam is often a disadvantage since it needs to be carefully aimed. If the distance between the transmitter and receiver is to be increased, it is best to increase the intensity of radiation by using up to 4 LEDs, wired in parallel, and passing 150mA each. Values for R1 are:

No. of LEDs	Resistance (ohms)	Power Intermittent use (W)	Intermittent and continuous use (W)
2	27	1	3
3	18	1	7
4	15	3	7

Chapter 4

DESIGNING NEW MODULES

Although there are over 60 modules in this book and they can be put together to build thousands of different systems, sooner or later you will find that you need a new module. Perhaps it will be one that is almost the same as one in the book. Often you can get ideas for new modules by modifying the modules presented here. Perhaps it will be something entirely novel. You may see a simple circuit or part of a circuit in a magazine and can base your new module on this. Learning to think in terms of modules will help you pick out useful parts of published circuits.

Until you become more experienced in electronics and can design and build circuits from scratch, the best approach is to work from the 'known' to the 'unknown'. Start with a module or circuit that you *know* will work, and build it on a breadboard. Then modify it *slightly*. For example, replace a resistor with one of a different value, or put in a thermistor instead of a light-dependent resistor, or change one type of logic gate for another of a different type. At each stage of modification check the working of the circuit. If it is still working, you can carry on and change it further. If it is not working, try to find out *why* not. Make changes accordingly. In this way it is often quite easy to arrive step-by-step at a completely new module.

A breadboard is invaluable when you are developing new modules, before you build them into permanent form. The breadboard need not be a large one; a board with, say, 350 sockets is big enough. Preferably it should have a row of connected sockets at top and bottom, possibly along each edge as well, for use as power supply rails. It should have one or more 7.5mm (0.3in) gaps between the panels of connectors so that it is able to take integrated circuits with up to 20 pins.

As well as a breadboard, you need several dozen lengths of insulated wire, ranging from about 3cm to about 10cm long. Preferably the insulation should be of several different colours, to make it easier to distinguish one wire from another in a

148

complicated circuit. Strip the insulation from about 7mm at each end. One thing is most important — the wire *must be single-stranded* wire. It is almost impossible to push multi-stranded wire into a breadboard socket. The wire often sold as 'hook-up wire' or 'bell-wire' is usually multi-stranded, and is *not* suitable for breadboarding.

Wire is usually specified in catalogues by giving the number of strands and their diameter, in millimetres. If you see '7/0.2', for example, it means that the wire is made up of 7 strands of wire, each 0.2mm in diameter. The best wire to use for breadboarding and, incidentally, for making all wired connections on modules, is specified as '1/0.6'.

As well as plain wires it is useful to have half-a-dozen lengths of single-stranded wire, about 10cm long, stripped at one end and with a crocodile clip soldered at the other. These are handy for making connections to the power supply, other modules, and larger off-board components such as relays.

As time goes by, you will gradually build up a collection of re-usable components for breadboarding, but you need a basic assortment to begin with. This list covers the main items that are likely to be useful:

1) Resistors
Carbon film resistors, 0.25W or 1/3 watt, 5% tolerance. Alternatively, use metal film resistors, 0.6W. You require several resistors of each of a variety of values. One way of beginning is to buy a 'starter pack', but these can be expensive and include far more than you really need to begin with. If you see 'special offers' of 'bargain' packs at low prices, try to check exactly what you are getting before you buy. Such packs may contain lots of resistors of one value and few of some other values. They may include large numbers of high-wattage types, which are not really of much use for module-building. They may be of low tolerance, perhaps only 20%. The most economical way to equip yourself is to buy 5 or 10 resistors of each of the following values: 100 ohms, 1k, 10k, 100k, 1M.

You may decide to include these intermediate values too: 470 ohms, 4k7, 47k, 470k, 4M7.

When breadboarding, it is easy to obtain other values simply by putting two resistors in series or in parallel. The rules for combining two resistors are simple. For two resistors in series (Fig.98) the combined resistance is the sum of the two individual resistors. For two resistors in parallel, the combined resistance is given by:

$$R = \frac{R_1 \times R_2}{R_1 + R_2}$$

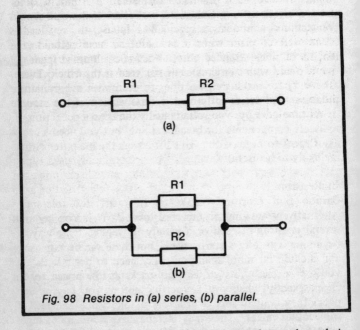

Fig. 98 Resistors in (a) series, (b) parallel.

If the two resistors in parallel are equal in value, their combined resistance is *half* their individual resistance. For example, you can make 2000 ohms by using two resistors of 1000 ohms in series. If your new circuit works with this combination, it will probably work with a single resistor of 2200 ohms (2k2). When you build the final version of the module on stripboard or a pcb, use a single resistor of this value in place of the two in series. Similarly, two 1000-ohm

150

resistors in parallel are equivalent to a single resistor of 500 ohms. These can be replaced with a single resistor of 470 ohms when you build the circuit permanently.

It is also useful to have a few 560-ohm resistors to limit the current through LEDs, when operating on 9V supply.

For variable resistors, buy one of each of the following values of rotary carbon potentiometer: 1k, 10k, 100k, 1M.

Cut the spindle short and secure a plastic knob to the spindle. Solder a lead to each of the three terminals, using single-stranded wire, and strip the insulation from the other ends of the leads. Preferably, the insulation of the wire should be coloured as shown in Figure 28. In use, the red lead is connected to the positive rail, the blue lead is connected to the 0V rail and the variable output voltage is obtained from the white lead. Output increases as the knob is turned clockwise. These variable resistors may be replaced with sub-miniature horizontal preset resistors in the final version of the module if the resistance does not often need to be adjusted.

2) Capacitors
Keep a stock of two or three of these commonly used types: 10n metallised polyester film; 100n metallised polyester film; 10μ electrolytic, axial leads; 100μ electrolytic, axial leads.

These cover the majority of coupling, decoupling and timing applications.

3) Diodes
1N4148 is the most frequently used type. You also need a few light-emitting diodes.

4) Transistors
The ZTX300 npn transistor is the one most generally used in this book. It has a gain of about 150 and can carry a current of up to 500mA.

5) Integrated Circuits
These allow you to build a wide range of circuits, though possibly you may need one or two other logic ics as well, depending on your special interests:

Operational amplifier: 7611
Timer: 7555
Logic: 4011 (quadruple 2-input NAND gate)
       4001 (quadruple 2-input NOR gate)
       4029 counter/divider
       4013 dual D-type flip-flop.

6) Switches

A few switches and push-buttons, with single-stranded wire leads soldered to them, the other ends of the leads being stripped.

With these components to hand you are ready to start designing new modules.

Chapter 5

ELECTRONIC SYSTEMS

In this chapter we look at a number of typical electronic systems built from the modules described in Chapter 3. Study these systems, noting the design points mentioned in connection with each. Try assembling some of the systems from the modules. Try adapting some of the systems by substituting other modules, or by adding further modules. After a short while, you will be well under way to designing and building systems of your own.

The examples of systems are arranged under headings, according to their function.

1 Timing Systems

Under this heading we consider systems that indicate when a fixed period of time has elapsed, and systems that measure the length of a given period.

An example of the first type is the familiar 'egg-timer'. This is set to trigger an alarm or make a lamp flash after a fixed period of time, say, 4 minutes. This is but one instance of what is generally termed a *process timer*. Such devices can be used for timing processes such as developing a film, baking a cake, or playing a move in chess. The timer tells you when 'time is up'.

There are many ways to make a process timer, which is perhaps why designs for process (usually egg-boiling!) timers appear so often in electronics magazines. The essential parts of such a system (see p.155) are:

Input — a control such as a push-button, for starting the timer.

Process — a module that operates for a fixed period of time, such as a *monostable* device.

Output — a suitable warning device to indicate 'time up'. The type that is best depends on the application. It might turn on a lamp, flash a lamp, sound a buzzer, or sound a single 'bleep'.

Of the modules described in this book, the obvious choice

153

for the timing is the monostable multivibrator (Module 43). With the components specified it times periods up to about 2 minutes long, so is suited for egg-timing and many other processes. For timing longer periods, it is possible to substitute a resistor of higher value for R1. Since this module already has a 'set' button for triggering the timer, it incorporates its own input stage and no separate input module is required. If you prefer a different type of input stage, such as a touch switch (Module 8), this could be connected to the input of Module 43.

The system as described so far (Fig.99a) is very simple to build but it suffers from a serious disadvantage, especially if the warning device is a buzzer, rather than a lamp. This is that the buzzer sounds *continuously* except during the actual timing period. It sounds while you are waiting to begin timing and there is no means of stopping it, once the period is over and the alarm has sounded, other than by switching off the power. It is more convenient to have some means of resetting it, silencing the buzzer while waiting for the timer to be used again. We will follow the further development of this system for using a buzzer effectively, though the system for driving a warning lamp is very similar.

Figure 99b shows a resettable timer. The system is triggered, as above, by pressing the button on Module 43. This starts the timer and its output goes high. At the end of the period, the output falls, triggering Module 51. We use O/P1 of this module to produce a brief low pulse which sets the bistable. O/P1 of the bistable turns on the transistor switch (Module 55), which makes the buzzer sound. The transistor switch is needed because the output from the bistable does not have the power to drive the buzzer directly. To silence the buzzer, we utilise the reset of Module 45, which resets the bistable.

An audible warning is more readily noticed if it sounds intermittently. Figure 99c shows how the system can be adapted to make the buzzer sound in this way. Again, this is just one of many possible ways of producing the effect. The astable multivibrator (Module 18) is set to oscillate at about 1Hz. The output from this is NANDed with the output of the bistable using one of the NAND gates of Module 44. Its output is inverted, using another of the gates, so the overall action of Module 44 is to AND the output (Fig.100). If the input

154

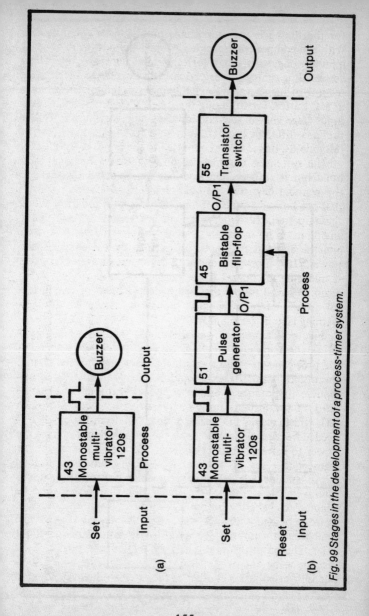

Fig. 99 Stages in the development of a process-timer system.

155

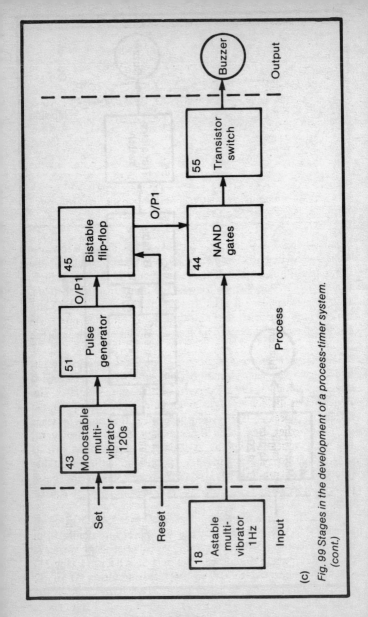

Fig. 99 Stages in the development of a process-timer system. (cont.)

156

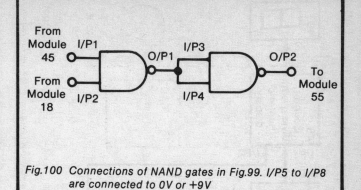

Fig.100 Connections of NAND gates in Fig.99. I/P5 to I/P8
are connected to 0V or +9V

from the flip-flop is low, the output of Module 44 is low, the
transistor switch is off and the buzzer is silent, whatever the
input from the astable. If the input from the flip-flop is high,
the output of Module 44 follows the input from the astable.
It goes high and low at 1Hz, turning the switch on and off and
making the buzzer sound intermittently at that rate. As
before, pressing the reset button of Module 45 silences the
buzzer.

Figure 101 shows a system for an elapsed-period timer,
which has the same function as a stop-watch. Timing is
based on Module 19, a crystal clock running at 2Hz. The
frequency is divided by 2, using Module 46, and this produces
a train of pulses at 1Hz. The precision of the timing pulses is
of a far higher order than the one-digit numeric display so,
from a practical viewpoint, it would be simpler and just as
satisfactory to replace Modules 19 and 46 with an astable
(Module 18) running at 1Hz. We have shown the more
precise module here in order to demonstrate how it can be
used.

The 1Hz signal is gated by one of the NAND gates of
Module 44. The other input to the NAND gate comes from
the bistable flip-flop which can be set or reset using two keys
on the key panel (Module 6). The pins at A1 and I1 (Fig.21)
are both connected to 0V so that pressing either S1 or S2
causes the bistable to be set or reset. This starts or stops the

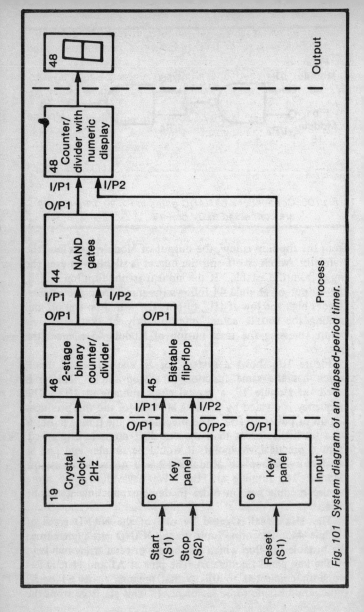

Fig. 101 System diagram of an elapsed-period timer.

158

train of pulses reaching the counter/divider (Module 48). When START is pressed, the display is incremented once each second.

Resetting, if required, is done by applying a high level to I/P2 of Module 48. A second key panel, with its pin at A1 connected to 9V, is used for this.

The two systems described above are both digital systems, but it is possible to design analogue systems also. The elapsed-period timer shown in Figure 102 has the merit of simplicity.

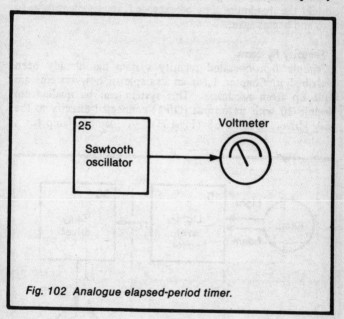

Fig. 102 Analogue elapsed-period timer.

The timing element is provided by Module 25, acting as a ramp generator. The value of C1 and the setting of VR1 are such that the output voltage rises from the valley point (see p.73) to the peak point is a suitable period of time. As a telephone call timer, for example, a convenient time would be 3 minutes. The voltmeter scale is re-graduated. You can fix a plain adhesive label to the outside of the plastic cover, if you do not wish to mark the internal scale. Mark the scale '0' at the valley

point and '3' at the peak point. Then subdivide the scale to
show minutes and half-minutes.

It is not easy to provide resetting for such a simple timer.
Discharging the capacitor is not allowable, since the circuit
would take an appreciable time to charge up to the valley point
voltage before the timing period begins. The simplest way of
using the timer is to wait until the needle suddenly flicks down
to the valley point, *then* begin timing. The needle then
gradually moves along the scale, showing the elapsed time.
Should the maximum time be exceeded, the needle returns to
zero and begins again.

2 Security Systems

A simple light-operated security system has already been
described in Chapter 1, as an example of how systems are
built up from modules.   This system can be made from
Module 10 with its output (O/P1) connected directly to the
relay driver, Module 58 (Fig.103).   A filament lamp (or a

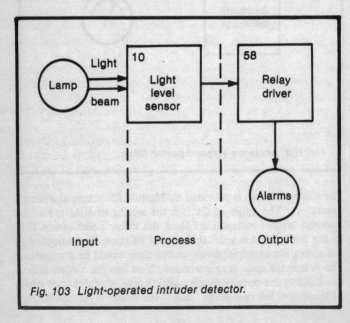

Fig. 103 Light-operated intruder detector.

160

window in daylight) provides a light source. The LDR of Module 10 receives this light and the output of the module is low. When the shadow of an intruder falls on the LDR, the output of Module 10 goes high, turning on the relay driver. The relay switch can be wired to operate one or more warning devices such as buzzers, bells, sirens and warning lamps.

The main disadvantages of such a system are (i) that the sensor uses a visible light beam, which can be seen and possibly avoided by the intruder, and (ii) that the alarm sounds only for as long as the beam is broken. If the intruder runs rapidly through the beam, the alarm sounds for only a fraction of a second, and may not be noticed. This is the point at which we start trying to improve the system.

The first disadvantage can be overcome by using infra-red. Module 64 provides a suitable source and Module 12 incorporates a sensor which responds preferentially to infra-red. The second disadvantage can be overcome by inserting a bistable flip-flop (Module 45) between the light sensor module and the relay driver. Module 45 produces a *high* pulse when the beam is broken, so the flip-flop must respond to a high trigger pulse. We use a 4001 to provide NOR gates for the flip-flop, as explained on p.112. Then even a very short high pulse from the light sensor is enough to set the bistable and turn on the relay. A button is connected to the reset input of the bistable to allow the system to be reset. This button is hidden where it can not be found by an intruder.

We leave it to the reader to design the modifications of the system needed to effect the above improvements.

Figure 104 illustrates a system that can be used for detecting sounds made by an intruder. It is particularly sensitive to bangs, creaks, and whistles, as well as to vibrations of the table on which the sound sensor is resting. The sensor could also be mounted on a window-frame or door. Other applications for this system are a baby-alarm and a telephone-bell repeater. The output from the sound sensor module is amplified and then fed to a diode pump. As explained on p.97, the output of the diode pump gradually rises as long as it is receiving an alternating input. An occasional sound of brief duration does not affect its output, so the odd creak (or baby's sneeze) is ignored. But any sound that lasts for an appreciable time

161

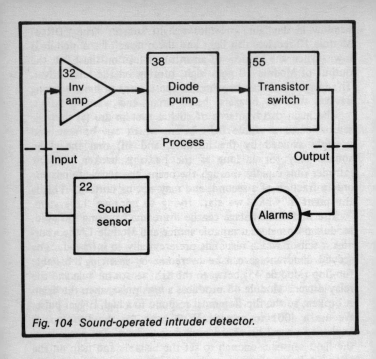

Fig. 104 Sound-operated intruder detector.

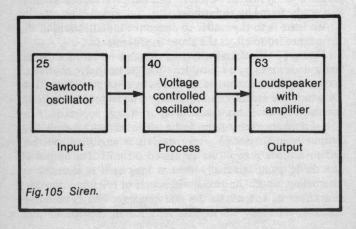

Fig.105 Siren.

raises the output voltage far enough to turn on the transistor switch and sound the alarm. The alarm circuit is not detailed in Figure 104. A solid-state audible warning device can be connected as the load of the transistor switch, or a relay can be used to switch on a more powerful electric bell or siren (see below).

As with the previous system, the alarm sounds only as long as sound is being received by the sensor. For a telephone-bell repeater, this normally results in the alarm sounding inter-mittently, in time with the bell. For a baby alarm or intruder alarm, it is an improvement to use a flip-flop module to trigger th alarm, which then continues to sound until the flip-flop is reset.

An alarm which has varying pitch is much more noticeable than a single-tone alarm. The siren in Figure 105 uses a saw-tooth oscillator (Module 25) to produce a voltage that ramps upward about once a second. This waveform is fed to a voltage controlled oscillator, which produces a repeated 'whooping' change in pitch. This siren can be connected to either of the systems shown in Figures 103 and 104, using a relay to switch on the current to the modules comprising the siren. Alternatively, these modules could be the load of a FET power switch (Module 57), the input of which comes from the light level sensor (Fig.103) or diode pump (Fig. 104).

If you prefer a two-tone alarm, substitute the astable multivibrator (Module 18) for the sawtooth oscillator. If this runs at about 0.5Hz, a two-tone 'dee-dar-dee-dar' sound is obtained. As an experimental variation on the siren of Figure 105, you could try substituting the sine-wave generator (Module 17) for the sawtooth oscillator. Depending on the frequency and amplitude of the generator output, a variety of warbling or 'air-raid-siren' effects can be heard.

A fire alarm system can detect fire in a number of ways: light, temperature, smoke. We use a temperature sensor for the system in Figure 106. The sensor is located where it will be most likely to detect an increased temperature. It might be just above a central heating boiler, or at the top of a stair-well, for example. The level is set by adjusting VR1 (Fig.34) so that it does not respond until the temperature exceeds normal

163

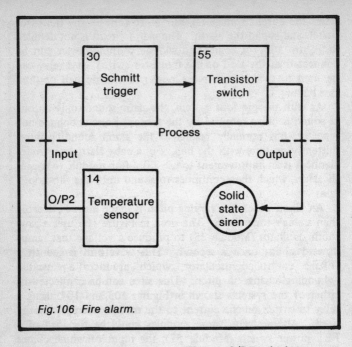

```
            ┌──────────────┐      ┌──────────────┐
     30      │              │  55  │              │
            │   Schmitt    │      │  Transistor  │
            │   trigger    │      │    switch    │
            └──────────────┘      └──────────────┘
                        Process
─ ─ ─                                              ─ ─ ─
    Input                              Output

           ┌──────────────┐
     14     │              │                  ┌──────┐
   O/P2     │ Temperature  │                  │ Solid│
           │   sensor     │                  │ state│
           └──────────────┘                  │ siren│
                                              └──────┘
```

Fig.106 Fire alarm.

maximum room temperature. We use O/P2, which increases
gradually as temperature rises. The next stage of the system is
a Schmitt trigger, so that, once the danger level has been
reached, the system is rapidly triggered and stays triggered
until there has been a considerable reduction in temperature
— something that will not happen if there really is a fire.
Thus we do not need a bistable flip-flop as was required in the
intruder-detection circuits. The transistor switch has a solid-
state siren as its load. These low-voltage, low-current devices
are an alternative to the alarms proposed for the other security
systems. Despite their modest power requirements they emit a
very loud noise.

3 Measurement Systems
The first two systems are for measuring temperature. They
operate in different ways and have been chosen to illustrate
important points about measurement systems. The simple

164

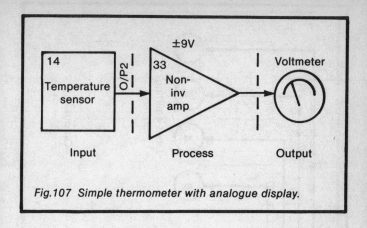

Fig.107 *Simple thermometer with analogue display.*

system in Figure 107 uses a thermistor as the heat sensitive element. As temperature rises, the voltage at O/P2 of Module 14 gradually rises. In order to give greater sensitivity the voltage is amplified by a non-inverting amplifier (Module 33). This is powered by ±9V so that it accepts positive voltages from Module 14 and its output can vary over the range 0–9V. The output is measured by a voltmeter. A meter with 10V full scale deflection is suitable.

Since the change in resistance of a thermistor is not linear with respect to temperature, it is not possible to perform any simple calculation to relate voltage to temperature. The voltmeter must be *calibrated*. Place the system in the coldest surroundings that it is to operate in. Leave it for 10 minutes to reach ambient temperature, then adjust VR1 of Module 14 to give a low output voltage. Measure the temperature with another thermometer. Mark the scale of the voltmeter at the position indicated by the needle. At this stage mark it temporarily in pencil. Repeat the operation with the system in the warmest conditions it is to operate in. You may find that the voltmeter needle has moved off the scale, because the gain of the amplifier is too high. If so, reduce the gain by adjusting VR1 of Module 33. Or you may find that the needle has moved only a short distance, because gain is too low. If so, increase the gain.

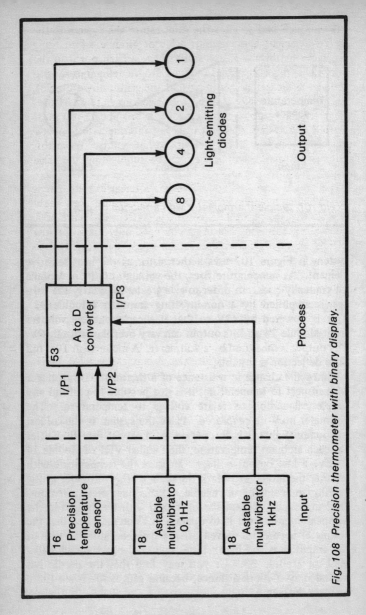

Fig. 108 *Precision thermometer with binary display.*

166

If you have had to alter the gain, return the system to the cold environment and re-adjust VR1 of Module 14 to bring the needle to the mark previously made. Then put it in the warm place, mark the scale, and measure the temperature with another thermometer (assuming that the gain is now suitable). You now have the scale marked with two known temperatures but, since the response of thermistor is not linear, you must now put the system in other places at intermediate temperatures and mark the scale at several other points. When this is done, the marks will guide you in subdividing the scale permanently into degrees.

The sensor used in Figure 108 has a linear output that is easy to relate to temperatures in degrees Celsius. You could use this in place of Module 14 for the system in Figure 107. This makes calibration easier as you need only mark the low and high point on the scale and then subdivide it evenly into degrees.

The main feature of Figure 108 is that it has a digital display of four LEDs. This is rather a rudimentary way of displaying temperature but it illustrates the principle of using an A-to-D converter. The system requires two astable multi-vibrators, a fast one (about 1kHz is suitable) for clocking the converter ic, and a slow one (about 0.1Hz) to start the conversion routine and up-date the display every 10 seconds. The display is intended to show the temperature in degrees in binary form. The range is $0°C$ to $15°C$. Since the output of Module 16 is 0V at $0°C$ and is 0.15V at $15°C$, and Module 53 accepts an input of 0V to 0.15V for full scale reading, the output of Module 16 can be fed directly to the converter. Module 16 has a low output impedance and Module 53 has a high input impedance so there is no problem about imped-ance matching. In measurement circuits using other sensors, it may be necessary to insert either a voltage follower (Module 34) or a non-inverting amplifier (Module 33) between the sensor module and the converter.

The light meter system in Figure 109 illustrates further points about measurement systems. The output voltage of Module 13 varies linearly with incident light over a reasonable range, but its value for any given light level depends on the setting of VR1. By adjusting VR1 we can make the meter

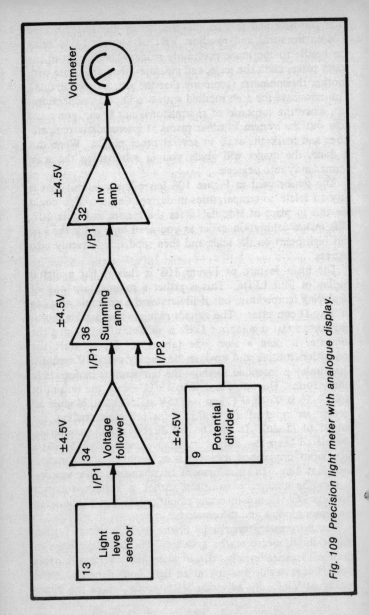

Fig. 109 Precision light meter with analogue display.

operate linearly over a particular range of light intensity. The output of the sensor is fed to a voltage follower and then to a summing amplifier. The summing amplifier also receives an input from a potential divider which can be set to any voltage between $-4.5V$ and $+4.5V$. This allows any voltage up to 4.5V to be added to or subtracted from the voltage from the sensor. The purpose of this amplifier is to provide for an *offset*, or zero adjustment. It allows for any desired output voltage from the sensor to be made to correspond with zero volts on the voltmeter. For example if the output from the sensor (and also from the voltage follower) is V_{IN}, and the reference voltage from the potential divider is V_{REF}, the output from the summing amplifier is $-(V_{IN} + V_{REF})$. Note the minus sign, and remember that V_{REF} can be positive or negative. The offset also compensates for offset errors at the inputs of the other amplifiers.

The inverting amplifier is used to adjust the gain of the system so that the voltmeter needle moves to full scale deflection when the sensor is receiving the maximum intended illumination. If the gain of the amplifier is A, its output is $A(V_{IN} + V_{REF})$. The negative sign has disappeared since the amplifier re-inverts the voltage.

This system is applicable to a wide variety of sensor modules. If you know the range of V_{OUT} over the range of illumination for which the meter is intended to operate, you can decide appropriate values for V_{REF} and A. It may be necessary to substitute resistors of other values for VR1 and R2 in Module 32 so as to allow the gain to be set to the right level with precision. In many instances you may find that the required offset voltage is within the range 0–1.26V. In this case greater precision in setting the reference voltage is obtained by using the voltage reference (Module 23) instead of Module 9. Since it will be operating on a 4.5V supply and only a small current is required, substitute a 2k7 resistor for R1. A negative reference voltage can be obtained by 'inverting' the module (see Fig.48):

(i)   connect D1 the other way round, with its cathode (k) to the 0V rail;

(ii) connect the 0V rail to the 0V of the system;

(iii)   connect the '+9V' rail to the −4.5V rail.

A negative reference voltage, from 0V to −1.26, is then obtainable from the output of the module.

4 Audio Systems

To begin with, let us look at a very simple system (Fig.110), a single-tone door alert. It could equally well be used as an alert for an invalid or elderly person, or as a morse-code

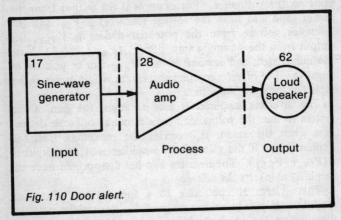

Fig. 110 Door alert.

practice set. The sound is turned on and off by switching the power on and off. The sine-wave generator gives a pleasant tone, though the astable multivibrator (Module 18) of saw-tooth generator (Module 25) could be used instead. The output from the generator is fed to an audio amplifier, which has a loudspeaker coupled to it through a capacitor.

Figure 111 shows a more elaborate door alert system that produces a series of notes when triggered. The audio signal is generated by a voltage-controlled oscillator (VCO). To produce the 'chimes' we have to apply to the VCO a voltage that varies in steps, each step corresponding to one note of the 'chimes'. Modules 49 and 36 produce the stepping voltage. Module 49 has 8 outputs, that are normally at logic low but a different *one* of these outputs goes high each time the device is clocked. We use four outputs to produce a 4-note chime.

170

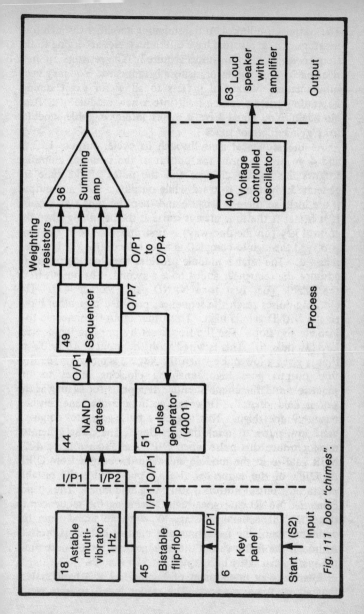

Fig. 111 Door "chimes".

The outputs are linked to the summing amplifier through four resistors. These resistors have different values according to the frequencies of the four notes required. The resistors are best selected by trial and error, using a breadboard. You may need sub-miniature horizontal presets to allow for exact tuning. Later the resistors can be built into a new module — a 'Tune Module'. You could have a set of interchangeable modules for playing different tunes.

As the sequencer runs through its cycle, outputs 1, 2, 3 and 4 go high in turn, the output of the summing amplifier follows the voltage changes and the notes of the tune are generated. Nothing is heard while outputs 5 to 7 and output 0 are high, so there is a pause and then the tune starts again. It is better if the tune always starts at the beginning when the control key (on the doorway) is first pressed, and if the tune is played through to completion after the control key has been released. The astable module provides the clocking pulses to advance the sequencer about once a second. The output from the astable goes first to a NAND gate (Module 44). The clocking pulses reach the sequencer provided that other input to the NAND gate is high. This other input is connected to a bistable flip-flop. The flip-flop is set by pressing the control key (Module 6). This is wired with the input at I1 to 0V so that it gives a low pulse when the key S2 is pressed. The flip-flop output goes high, enabling clocking pulses to the sequencer and the chime sounds. It repeats for as long as the key is held pressed. However, each time the tune finishes, output 7 goes high. This triggers a pulse-generator to give a brief low pulse to reset the flip-flop. The pulse generator must produce this pulse when O/P7 *rises*, so we use a 4001 NOR gate ic in the module and take the output from O/P1. As O/P7 of the sequencer rises, a pulse resets the bistable unless the control button is still being held down. The output from the NAND gate goes high, advancing the sequencer to stage '0'. It remains at stage '0', with no sound from the oscillator, until the next time the control button is pressed. Although the figure shows the arrangement for a 4-note tune, the system can easily be adapted for 5 or 6 notes.

The one-way inter-comm of Figure 112 is a basic system that allows for expansion. The reader is left to improve it,

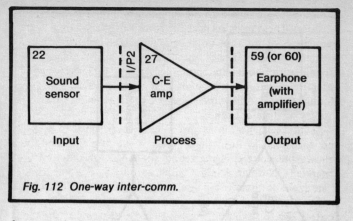

Fig. 112 One-way inter-comm.

for example, by making it a two-way system, providing calling tones, and giving it loudspeaker output.

Figure 113 shows AM medium-wave radio receiver sets of varying degrees of complexity and sensitivity. All are based on the same receiver module. At (a) we have the simplest system, capable of giving earphone reception with a reasonably powerful local station. Version (b) is similar but gives slightly better reception. Version (c) has a 3-transistor amplifier, which provides enough power for a loudspeaker. The active low-pass filter is optional but improves the sound quality. The signal from the radio receiver module has an excess of high frequencies and the use of the filter gives more emphasis to the bass. These systems are but a few of the many that can be constructed from the selection of amplifier modules contained in this book.

The system of Figure 114 is experimental in the sense that you may need to try various combinations of modules to get it working properly. The sound sensor can be replaced by the radio receiver module. The audio signal is amplified and its output is used to power a filament lamp. The average output of the amplifier is 0V relative to the 0V rail, or 4.5V relative to the -4.5V rail. A suitable lamp is a 3.5V torch bulb with connection between the amplifier output and the -4.5V rail. The lamp will glow brightly, but its brightness varies imperceptibly owing to the audio signal. For transmission over a

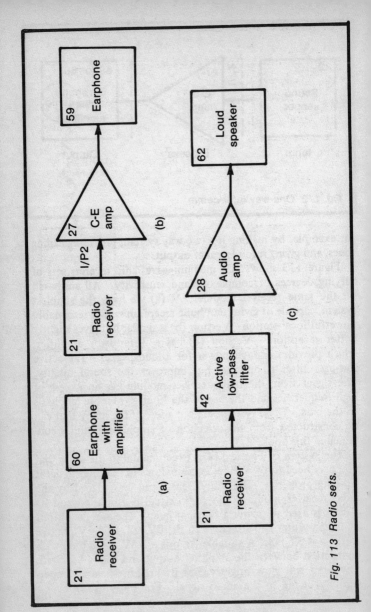

Fig. 113 Radio sets.

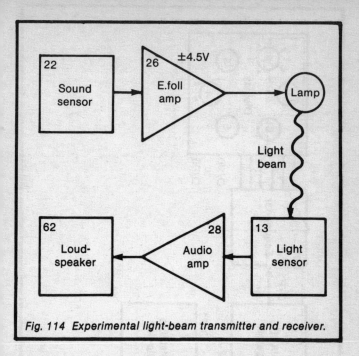

Fig. 114 Experimental light-beam transmitter and receiver.

distance you will need to place a lens in front of the lamp to focus the light into a beam. Another way of obtaining a beam is to adapt a reflector torch. You may find that a low-value resistor in series with the lamp reduces the brightness but makes the audio signal relatively stronger.

The phototransistor sensor is the best light sensor to use as it is capable of responding at high frequency. Preferably, mount the phototransistor at the end of a tube (about 10cm long) to prevent light from other sources falling on it. A lens could be used to concentrate the beam on to the phototransistor. The output from the light sensor is a steady voltage with the audio signal superimposed on it. Module 28 amplifies the audio signal and sound is heard from the loudspeaker.

5 Games Systems

The roulette game (Fig.115) is a pseudo-random device that

175

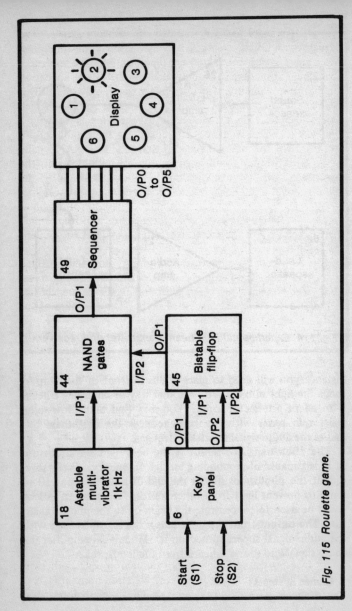

Fig. 115 Roulette game.

can be used in place of a six-sided die in many games. The display has 6 LEDs, only one of which is lit at any one time. When the start button is pressed, the outputs of the sequencer go high in turn, but so rapidly that all the LEDs appear to glow gently. When the stop button is pressed, only one LED is lit. The action is so fast that it is impossible to know which LED will be lit. Thus the effect is just the same as throwing a 6-sided die. The sequencer is clocked by the astable multivibrator, but the pulses from this first pass to a NAND gate. If the other input to the gate is low no pulses pass to the sequencer, which is held with one of its outputs high. If the other input is high, pulses pass at 1kHz and the sequencer goes through its cycle 167 times a second. The controlling input to the NAND gate comes from the bistable flip-flop, which can be set by pressing the start button, and reset by pressing thes stop button.

The key panel is wired up with pins A1 and I1 connected to the 0V rail. Thus they give the low inputs required to set and reset the bistable. The outputs of the sequencer are connected to the anodes of the LEDs. The cathodes of the LEDs are all connected to 0V.

Current-limiting resistors are not needed. On the sequencer module, switch S6 is closed so that the ic is reset as output 6 goes high.

The display can take many forms. For roulette, the LEDs are arranged as shown in the figure. As well as its use as a die, the system can be used to play a gambling game which is a variation of roulette. In this game S7 is closed instead of S6. If the system is stopped while O/P6 is high, no LED is lit. Players bet on:

(i)   a 'number', 1 to 6 – the bank pays 6 to 1;
(ii) 'odds plus' (1, 2 or 3, 4 or 5, 6) – the bank pays 3 to 1;
(iii) 'odds or evens' (1, 3, 5 or 2, 4, 6) – the bank pays 2 to 1.

In (i) you win if your selected number appears, otherwise you lose. In (ii) you win if your selected odd number (1, 3 or 5) appears or your odd number plus 1 (2, 4 or 6) appears. In

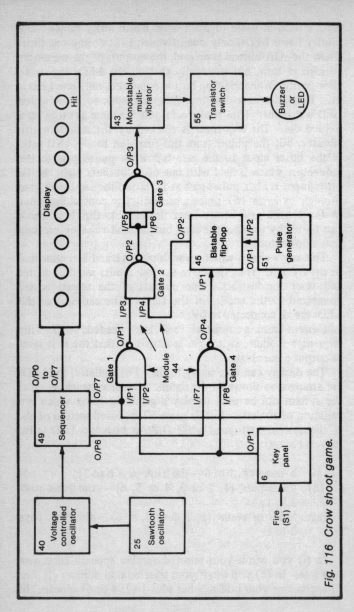

Fig. 116 Crow shoot game.

(iii) you select 'odd' or 'even' and win if any number of the correct kind appears. The bank wins all stakes if no LED lights, so the odds of the game are weighted in favour of the bank. The bank changes hands on every third 'no LED'.

The crow shoot game (Fig.116) tests your timing skills. The display represents the flying crow by a row of LEDs which are lit one at a time, in sequence from left to right. You have to hit the crow when it reaches the right-hand end of the display, i.e. when the 8th LED is lit. You can not cheat by holding down the fire button and waiting for the crow to reach the 8th LED. If the button is down when the 7th LED is lit, you are not able to score for that round.

The LEDs are lit in turn by the outputs from the sequencer module. The LEDs can simply be connected with their anodes to one of the outputs O/P0 to O/P7 and their cathodes to the 0V rail. The sequencer is driven by pulses from the voltage-controlled oscillator and the rate at which this oscillates is controlled by the sawtooth oscillator. This runs slowly but causes the crows to change their speed as they move along the display, thus making the game more difficult. By altering the basic frequency of the VCO you can make the crows fly faster or slower. By altering the frequency of the sawtooth oscillator you can control the rate at which speed changes. This gives you two controls over the difficulty level of the game.

The fire button is S1 of the key panel. Terminal pin A1 of this panel is connected to 9V so pressing the key causes a high level to appear at the NAND gates 1 and 4. The other input of gate 1 is connected to O/P7 of the sequencer. If the fire button is pressed while this output is high (i.e. the 8th LED is lit), it counts as a *hit*. OP/1 of Module 44 goes low. The I/P3 goes low and, provided that I/P4 is high, O/P2 goes high. This is inverted by gate 3, so O/P3 goes low, triggering the monostable. This is set to give a pulse about half a second long and turns on a transistor switch. The switch has a lamp or a solid state buzzer as its load, so the LED flashes or the buzzer beeps, to register the hit.

However, if the fire button is pressed while O/P6 is high, O/P4 of Module 44 goes low, counting as a *miss*. This triggers the bistable flip-flop, and its O/P2 goes low. This

179

prevents a later 'hit' from triggering the monostable. O/P7 of the sequencer triggers a pulse generator as it goes low at the end of the sequence, this resets the flip-flop ready for the next flight of the crow. Firing when the first 6 LEDs are lit carries no penalties and you still have a chance to fire at the 8th LED.

To play this game, watch the LEDs and try to press the fire button while the 8th LED is lit, *not before*. Count the number of times you fire the button and how many bleeps (hits) you hear. Try to score 10 bleeps with 10 consecutive shots.

With a few more modules it is possible to count the score automatically, and display it either in binary code or as a 7-segment numeral.

6 Remote Control Systems

The systems all make use of infra-red radiation, produced by the infra-red transmitter (Module 64). The range of control may be maximised by having up to 4 LEDs in the transmitter, as explained on page 147. Use the push-button (S2) to activate the transmitter. The simplest system is shown in Figure 117. The sensor has an infra-red diode and when infra-red radiation reaches it, its output goes high. This turns on a transistor switch. What happens next depends on the application. The load of the transistor switch can be a lamp, a motor, a relay or a solenoid. Switching this activates the device. It may move the arm of a robot, start the motor or turn the steering gear of a model vehicle, or switch off the connection to a loudspeaker, thus muting a tape-recorder or radio set. There are dozens of possibilities. Figure 117 shows Module 55 doing the switching, but it is equally possible to use Module 56 for reverse action, or Modules 57 or 58 for heavier loads. The output of Module 12 could control several modules at once, switching off some devices and switching on others.

Figure 118 shows how the range of control can be further extended by making the sensor even more responsive to slight changes in infra-red. In this the output from the sensor is fed to a comparator (Module 37). The sensor output is compared with a reference voltage from a potential divider that is part of the module (VR1). The comparator (Module

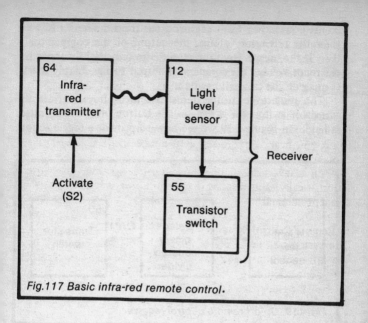

Fig.117 Basic infra-red remote control.

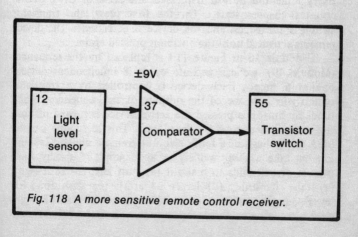

Fig. 118 A more sensitive remote control receiver.

37) is powered by ±9V. If the output from the sensor is lower than the reference voltage, the output of the comparator is 0V. If the output from the sensor rises only slightly above the reference voltage the comparator output swings sharply to 9V, turning on the transistor switch.

The remote control systems described above activate the transistor switch for as long as the button on the transmitter is held. In Figure 119 we see how to provide a toggle action.

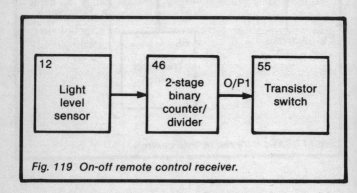

Fig. 119 On-off remote control receiver.

The output from the sensor goes to a 2-stage binary count. Every time the button is pressed, the state of O/P1 of the counter changes state. On the first press, the transistor switch is turned on and the device is activated. The device remains activated until the button is pressed again.

If Module 46 in Figure 119 is replaced by the sequencer (Module 49), we can activate up to 8 independent devices one at a time. Each device is controlled by a transistor switch wired to one of the outputs of the sequencer. Each time the button is pressed the active device is turned off and the next in sequence is turned on. This technique can be used as the basis of a fairly elaborate remote control system. Let us take a robot vehicle as an example. It may have motors or solenoids to make it (a) turn left; (b) turn right; (c) raise its arms; (d) lower its arms; (e) flash its LED 'eyes'. Five outputs of the sequencer (O/P0 to O/P4) are used to initiate these operations. Switch S5 of the sequencer is closed to make it reset when O/P5 goes high. If the button is pressed repeatedly and fairly slowly, the operations each happen one after another. But, if the button is pressed and pressed again quickly, any of the operations can be skipped over. For example, if it is turning left and we want it to raise its arms, we press the button twice. For an instant it starts to turn right, but the button is pressed again so quickly that this phase is too short to be noticed. By careful pressing of the button, the robot may be made to turn left and right alternately, without giving it time to raise or lower its arms or to flash its 'eyes'. The effect of alternate left and right turns is to make it move straight ahead. In these and other ways the binary counter, the sequencer and bistable flip-flops can be used in remote control to effect a wide range of actions.

Chapter 6

BUILDING ELECTRONIC SYSTEMS

Building electronic systems from modules you have already constructed is simply a matter of connecting together the modules with crocodile clips. You can, of course, make permanent use of a system composed of individual modules but usually it is preferable for the sake of tidiness and compactness to assemble the system on a single circuit-board. This chapter deals with ways of building systems into a permanent single-board form.

Planning the System

Before you begin building a system permanently on one board, assemble it from separate modules. Thorough testing at this stage ensures that the permanent version of the system will work properly and perform as intended. By examining the inputs and outputs of each module when it is part of the system, you can more easily locate faults. If the system does not work as well as you had hoped, it gives you a chance to substitute one module for another of the same type, to see which gives better performance. For example, you may not be sure which type of light sensor to use for a given purpose. Building the system from separate modules first allows you to test the performance of each type of light sensor for its intended application.

At this stage you will probably not have all the modules already built. There is no need to build them on stripboard specially for trying out the system. Any that you do not already have can be assembled on a breadboard, and included in the prototype system. You may also want to try out modifications to the original module designs, or invent completely new modules of your own. These too can be breadboarded at this stage.

Simplifying the System

When you have put together the whole system, tested it and found that it does its job properly, the next stage is to transfer the system to a single board. If you are adept at designing pcbs, you are now in for a long and interesting session. Although the individual modules may take up a lot of board space, it may be possible to lay out the system in a compact way on a relatively small pcb.

Whether you are putting the system onto a pcb or onto a stripboard, there is some simplification that must first be done. The modules have been designed so that they are capable of being used in a number of different ways. Many of them have more than one input, and several outputs. For example, most of the amplifier modules have two inputs — one direct and one by way of a coupling capacitor. Only one of these will be needed in your system. For slowly changing voltage levels, as found in measuring systems, you need the direct input. For audio systems, you need the capacitor input. The unwanted input is omitted from the final system. Many of the sensor modules (for example, Module 10) have a direct output from the sensor (O/P2) and another output from a built-in transistor switch (O/P1). Decide which output you will use; if you are not using the transistor switch output, you are able to eliminate the transistor and two resistors from the system which are now redundant. This cuts costs, simplifies wiring and board space, and makes pcb design easier.

Several of the logic modules have inputs that are held high or low by pull-up or pull-down resistors. This is to allow such inputs to assume a 'default' state in temporary systems without the need to connect any input device to them. For example, in the bistable flip-flop (Module 45), there are 15k pull-up resistors on the inputs. These are necessary if the inputs are to be operated by push-buttons. However, in some systems, these inputs are operated by the outputs from other logic ics. In the crow shoot game system in Figure 116, the flip-flop is operated by outputs from a pulse generator and a NAND gate. There is no need for pull-up resistors in this case, since the high outputs from the pulse generator and NAND gate have the identical effect. Although the resistors make no difference to the operation of the circuit in this system, they are not needed and can be omitted.

Another point about the bistable flip-flop, and a number of other modules, is that it has a built-in indicator LED. You

185

may need this in your system, but probably you will not. If you do not need the indicator, the LED is not required and two of the gates of the ic are not used. These gates must not simply be left unconnected, for unconnected CMOS inputs usually cause the ic to behave erratically and may even result in it burning out:

All CMOS inputs must be connected either to the positive rail, the ground rail, or to a CMOS output.

It is important to remember this when using the NAND gate module (Module 44), for it is rarely that all four gates are used. In this connection it is possible to economise in the number of ics by using spare gates for other purposes. For example, if the system includes a bistable flip-flop and also uses one or two NAND gates, the two spare gates of the flip-flop module can supply the required NAND gates.

Several of the modules have d.i.l. switches to allow the modules to be used for a number of different functions. For example Module 47 has switches to allow it to count up or down and in binary or BCD mode. In any given system it will be counting in one direction and in one mode, so these switches can be eliminated. The pins to which these switches were previously connected can then be wired directly either to the +9V rail or the 0V rail, depending on whether their input is to be high or low. Pull-up or pull-down resistors are omitted. With the sequencer (Module 49) only one wired connection is required from the reset pin to the 0V rail or to one of the outputs. This eliminates the need for the fairly expensive d.i.l. switch and a considerable amount of wiring.

Transferring to Stripboard

Since almost all the modules are designed to fit on to a board 15 holes by 16 strips, it is easy to transfer a system to a long board, 16 strips wide. The modules are set out side-by-side on the board with the power rails running the full length of the board at the top and bottom edges (Fig.120a). At the most, the board has to be 15 holes long for each module it holds. Thus the 3-module system in Figure 106 would need a maximum of 45 holes (3 x 15), the solid state siren being mounted off-board. However, owing to the fact that some modules (e.g. the precision temperature sensor) have few components

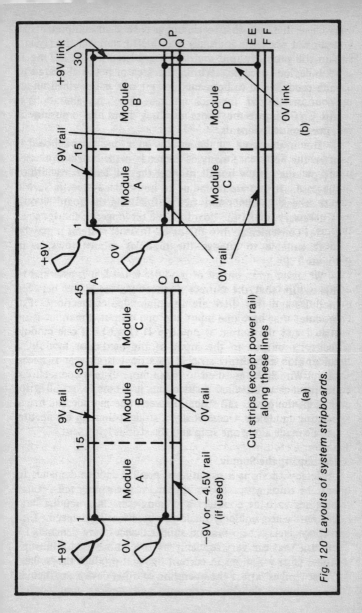

Fig. 120 Layouts of system stripboards.

187

and that it is possible to eliminate redundant components as described above, it is usually possible to compact the layout. You will probably find that the board need not be as long as 15 holes per module. Within the area of board allocated to each module the components are set out as described under *Stripboard layout* for each module. The only alterations to this arrangement are those resulting from the omission of redundant components.

The arrangement of the system on a long narrow board is often the best, since many of the ready-made instrument cases accept long narrow boards running the full length or width of the case. If you are intending to house the system in such a case, check its dimensions before finalizing the board layout. If necessary, make the board a little bit longer or shorter so as to slot conveniently into the case. In other systems it may be more suitable to arrange the modules in two rows, as in Figure 120b.

Whatever arrangement of modules is used, it is essential to make sure that the correct connections are made between modules and that there are no unintended connections. For modules that have one input and one output, the input is on strip I and the output is on strip H (Fig.6). If one module feeds its output to the input of the next-door module, a solder-blob connecting strip H to strip I is all that is necessary. Wire links are used to make more distant connections. To prevent unintended connections it is best to cut all strips (except the power rail strips) between one module and neighbouring modules. Occasionally a straight-through connection can be made along one strip and the strip is left uncut.

Decoupling the Supply

In logic systems it is essential to prevent sudden demands for current causing 'spikes' to appear on the supply rails. Complex ics such as counters and converters may require large currents when suddenly made to operate at high speed. LED displays, relays, motors and similar devices have demands for current that can vary suddenly by several hundred milliamps. These large variations in current demand produce the 'spikes'. These 'spikes' affect the operation of other devices, particularly counters, flip-flops, registers and devices that contain registers, such as A-to-D converters. Their operation becomes highly erratic.

One way of avoiding this effect is to wire a large-value capacitor (say $1000\,\mu F$ or $2200\,\mu F$) between the points at which the positive and ground supply are connected to the board. This holds a ready 'store' of charge which helps even out the effects of varying demand for current. In addition, it is important to have smaller capacitors scattered over the board to absorb the spikes that are inevitably generated. We call these *decoupling capacitors*. Use polyester, ceramic disc, or metallised ceramic plate capacitors of 100n value. Modules 47 and 48 already include these, but in a larger system they should be present at the rate of one capacitor for every 5 logic ics. Connect each capacitor between the positive supply rail and the ground rail. Scatter them evenly over the board. If you are not sure exactly where to place them, give preference to locations close to spike-generating and spike-sensitive ics, such as timers, counters, flip-flops, and display drivers as well as to relay-drivers and power transistors. If a system is not working properly and the fault is traced to a spike-sensitive ic, an additional decoupling capacitor wired close to the supply terminals of the ic will do no harm and may possibly cure the trouble.

Appendix A

ELECTRONIC CIRCUIT SYMBOLS

The drawings shown in Figure 121 show the symbols used in electronic circuit diagrams. The names of the terminals are given in full. For a short explanation of what these components do, see Appendix B.

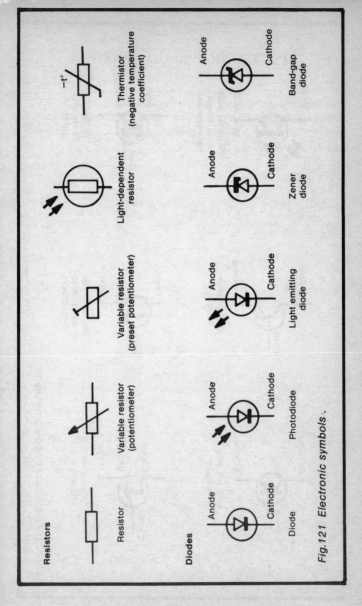

Fig.121 Electronic symbols.

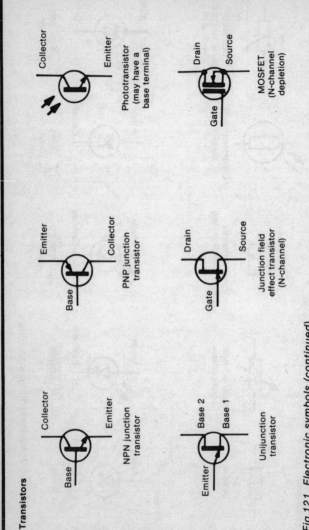

Transistors

Collector — Emitter

Phototransistor (may have a base terminal)

Emitter — Collector — Base

PNP junction transistor

Collector — Emitter — Base

NPN junction transistor

Drain — Source — Gate

MOSFET (N-channel depletion)

Drain — Source — Gate

Junction field effect transistor (N-channel)

Base 2 — Base 1 — Emitter

Unijunction transistor

Fig.121 Electronic symbols (continued).

192

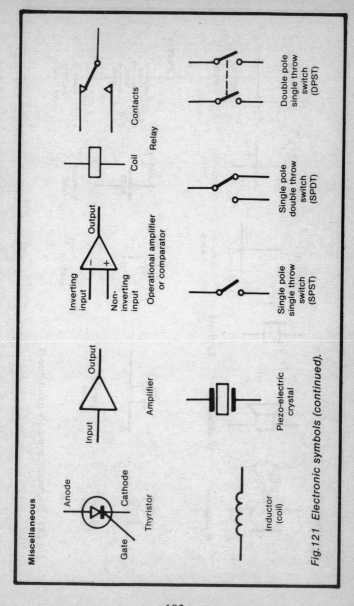

Fig.121 Electronic symbols (continued).

193

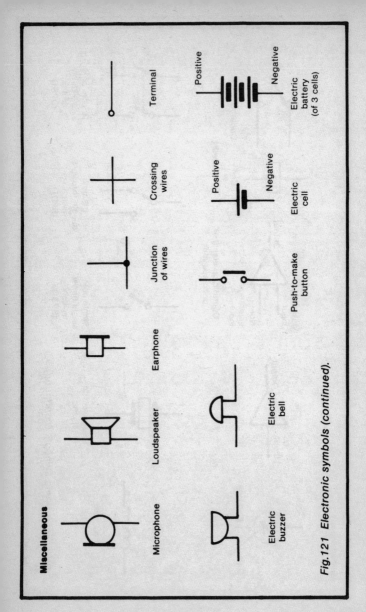

Fig.121 Electronic symbols (continued).

194

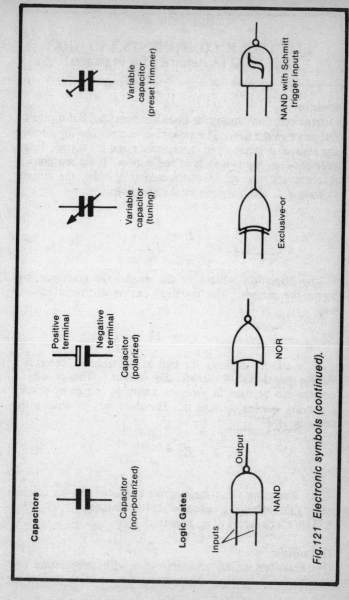

Capacitors

Capacitor (non-polarized)

Positive terminal
Negative terminal

Capacitor (polarized)

Variable capacitor (tuning)

Variable capacitor (preset trimmer)

Logic Gates

Inputs
Output

NAND

NOR

Exclusive-or

NAND with Schmitt trigger inputs

Fig.121 Electronic symbols (continued).

195

Appendix B

ELECTRONIC COMPONENTS AND WHAT THEY DO (A summary for beginners)

Resistor

Current can flow through it in either direction, but it offers a *resistance* to the flow. The amount of current flowing through the resistor depends upon its resistance and the voltage difference between the two ends of the resistor. If the resistance is R ohms and the voltage difference is V volts, the current flowing is I, which is given by the equation:

$$I = \frac{V}{R}.$$

The bigger the voltage or the smaller the resistance, the bigger the current. This equation can be written in another way:

$$V = IR.$$

If a current I flows through a resistance R, there is a voltage equal to IR across the resistor. This is why a resistor can be used to generate a varying voltage by passing a varying current through it. The third way of writing the equation is:

$$R = \frac{V}{I}.$$

By measuring the voltage across a resistor and the current passing through it, we can calculate its resistance.

Two special types of resistor are:

Thermistors

The resistance of all resistors varies with temperature but usually only slightly. Thermistors are made so that their resistance changes considerably, usually decreasing as temperature increases called "negative temperature coefficient".

Light-dependent Resistors
The resistance of an LDR decreases as the amount of light falling on it increases.

Capacitors
It consists of two metal plates, very close together, but insulated from one another by a non-conducting layer, the *dielectric*. The dielectric may be air, plastic, or a chemical substance. The capacitor stores electric charge — one plate has positive charge and the other has negative charge. The amount of charge that can be stored for a given voltage depends on the *capacitance* of the capacitor. This partly depends on the size of the plates. For large capacitance, the plates are rolled tightly together to give a large area in a relatively small volume. As current flows into a capacitor, more and more charge is stored and the voltage across the capacitor increases. As current flows out of a capacitor, charge is removed and the voltage across the capacitor is reduced.

When the potential of one plate of a capacitor is changed, the potential of the other plate changes too *by the same amount*, so as to keep the *difference* in potential (i.e. the voltage across the capacitor) the same. This is why an alternating voltage applied to one plate of a capacitor causes an alternating voltage to appear at the other plate. Used in this way, the capacitor *couples* one part of a circuit to another, even though the parts of the circuit are insulated from one another by the dielectric of the capacitor and no current actually flows from one part to the other.

Diodes
A semiconductor device with two terminals, anode (a) and cathode (k). Current can flow from the anode to the cathode but not in the reverse direction. There is an inherent potential difference across the diode; this is about 0.6V if the diode is made of silicon (most are), and 0.2V if it is made of germanium. The cathode is negative with respect to the anode. For a current to flow from anode to cathode this *forward voltage*

drop must be exceeded. The voltage across the diode must exceed 0.6V for a silicon diode to conduct in the forward direction.

Special kinds of diode include:

Zener diodes

This conducts current in the reverse direction (cathode to anode) when a given reverse voltage across the diode is exceeded. Zener diodes are made with different reverse voltages, e.g. 4.7V, 5.1V.

Photodiodes

This is normally used when reverse-biassed, i.e. the cathode is positive of the anode and no current flows. However, there is a very small *leakage current* in all diodes that are reverse-biassed and, in the case of the photodiode, the size of this current depends on the amount of light falling on the diode.

Light-emitting diodes

The LED emits light when a current flows through it in the forward direction. Most LEDs emit red light, but other types are available that emit orange, yellow or green light, or infra-red radiation. LEDs conduct in one direction, the same as ordinary diodes, but they are destroyed by reverse voltages larger than about 5V.

Transistors

The most common type is the npn bipolar junction transistor, such as the ZTX300. This is connected with its collector (c) positive of the other two terminals. No current flows from collector to emitter (e) until the base (b) is made positive of the emitter (but the base must not ever be positive of the collector). When current flows into the base terminal, it flows out of the emitter terminal. This causes current to flow into the collector terminal and out of the emitter terminal. The collector current is much larger than the base current and is proportional to it. The ratio between the collector current and the base current is called the *current gain* of the transistor. Typically this can be 100 to 200 times, and explains why a transistor is used for amplifying currents.

The junction between the base and emitter layers of the transistor forms a diode. Current can not flow from base to emitter until the forward voltage drop is exceeded, that is, until the base is 0.6V or more positive of the emitter for a silicon transistor.

Junction transistors can be made of silicon (usually) or germanium, and can be npn (usually) or pnp. The connections of the collector and emitter of a pnp transistor are the inverse of those of an npn transistor (see Module 25).

Field effect transistors consist of a conductive bar, *the channel*, through which the current flows. An electric current in metals and certain types of semiconductors is a flow of electrons (negatively charged particles) from negative to positive. In an FET they enter the transistor at the *source* terminal and leave it by the *drain* terminal. In terms of 'conventional current' which is considered as flowing from positive to negative, current flows from drain to source. The other terminal is the *gate* which surrounds the channel but is electrically insulated from it. No current can flow from the gate to the channel, but the charge on the gate produces an electric *field*. The strength of this field alters the effective width of the channel and hence its resistance to the flow of current through the channel. Only a microscopically small current is needed to affect the charge on the gate, yet the resulting field has a big effect on the amount of current flowing through the transistor. This *field effect* is used as the basis for amplification.

CMOS field effect transistors (or MOSFETs) operate on the same principle, but the gate is insulated from the channel by an exceedingly thin layer of silicon oxide. This layer is easily destroyed by high voltages, which is why special care is needed to avoid static charges when handling CMOS devices. One method of fabricating CMOS devices capable of carrying heavy currents is known as VMOS, and is used for power transistors.

Phototransistors are usually of the npn type. Light falling on the base-emitter junction has the same effect as a base current. It causes a large collector current to flow, proportional to the light intensity.

Integrated circuits
These consist of complete circuits consisting of tiny resistors, capacitors, diodes and transistors manufactured on a single chip of silicon. A single ic may contain dozens, hundreds or even thousands of individual components. There are so many types of integrated circuit and their internal circuitry is usually so complicated that it is difficult to begin to understand how they work. Given a particular set of inputs, they produce a particular set of outputs. The simplest instances of this input/output way of thinking are the truth tables of the logic gates (p.109). These specify exactly *what* the gates do but not *how* they do it. This 'black box' approach is the best one to adopt for integrated circuits. The descriptions of the modules explain what the ics do, without going into the details of how they work.